Bleeding Hear

WILLIAM SCAMMELL

C000093993

PETERLOO POETS

First published in 1992
by Peterloo Poets
2 Kelly Gardens, Calstock, Cornwall PL18 9SA, U.K.

© 1992 by William Scammell

All rights reserved. No part of this publication may be reproduced,
stored in a retrieval system, or transmitted, in any form or by any
means, electronic, mechanical, photocopying, recording or otherwise without the prior permission in writing of the publisher.

**A catalogue record for this book is available
from the British Library**

ISBN 1-871471-28-1

Printed in Great Britain by
Latimer Trend & Company Ltd, Plymouth

BLEEDING HEART YARD

by the same poet

Yes & No (Peterloo Poets, 1979)
A Second Life (Peterloo Poets, 1982)
Jouissance (Peterloo Poets, 1985)
Editor: *Between Comets: for Norman Nicholson at 70* (Taxus Press, 1985)
Eldorado (Peterloo Poets, 1987)
Keith Douglas: a study (Faber & Faber, 1987)
Editor: *The New Lake Poets* (Bloodaxe Books, 1991)

ACKNOWLEDGEMENTS to the editors of *Critical Quarterly*, *Gown*, *The Honest Ulsterman*, *Iron*, *The Jacaranda Review*, *Kenyon Review*, *London Magazine*, *Poetry Durham*, *Poetry Matters*, *PN Review*, *Poetry Review*, *Quartz*, *Times Literary Supplement*, *Verse*, in whose pages some of these poems first appeared.

'Dunmail Raise' won a Sotheby's Award in the 1987 Arvon International Poetry Competition, and was first published in the *1987 Anthology* (Arvon Foundation, 1989), selected by Ted Hughes and Seamus Heaney.

'The Emperor of China' was first published in *New Writing from the North* (MidNAG, 1988), ed. Dick Davies and David Williams.

'A World Elsewhere' won first prize in the 1989 National Poetry Competition, and was first published in the *1989 Prize Winners* anthology (Poetry Society, 1990).

'Green Over Blue' was first published in the *Poetry Book Society Anthology 1990-91* (Hodder & Stoughton, 1991), ed. Anne Stevenson.

Supported by

Cornwall
County Council

INVESTMENT
SOUTH WEST ARTS

Recipient of an Arts Council Incentive Funding Award

Contents

A World Elsewhere

1. THE VISIT
There were barns, paddocks,
young fruit trees coquetting
in the rain and thrum of wind.
It blew so hard the awning
of the outside love-seat split
a little further every hour.

Tall dogs with silky hair
slipped moorings by the Aga
gliding up to my strange scent;
the squash-faced semi-precious cat
subsided into a hump; and you
sat down, oblique and fine as
an old-fashioned stroke of the pen.

All the covers of the novels kiss.
Five chickens cluck in the yard
like perfect readers, wanting more
and more from the rich yawny air,
to which they held one claw up
in mid-strut. When the time came

you fed us all we needed,
baroque vespers after a light supper
of green salad and talk
served up with a rainbow trout.
I like your vestal nightie,
sloping eyes, big girlish feet
better than the small history
we made ourselves to make that night.

2. NOT MARBLE

Beatrice, Laura, and the Dark Lady are
discovered over a litter of tableware
with second cups of coffee, chocolate mints,
liqueurs, the viol's languid impudence.

Candour shines from each immortal eye.
Two handsome serving men are waved away.
Someone pulls out an exquisite handkerchief
and dabs her nose. They laugh, and laugh, and laugh.

3. KIEV (after Mandelstam)

Last night the army trundled out of town
on the last streetcar, hugging its wounded. One
great bloodstained overcoat was calling out
'Don't worry, we'll be back among you! Soon!'

Bleeding Heart Yard

Is where you go to buy the finest paper
gathered under an English sky.
The wiring looped up in the corner
is the scribbled ghost of Hokusai,
the rafters Dürer's signature.

They are keeping one eye on the rag trade
and one on the clientèle,
nails pointilliste in blue and red,
clothes flaring round them like a sail
let out to catch the lightest mood.

Nothing is lost either on the old Ralph
Roister Doister who mans the shop,
monkeying up to the topmost shelf
or naming the name of a fellowship
that's shy of people. 'Help yourself'

he says to the punters. They do and must,
stroking the paper as if it were
all the first things and the last,
a favourite daughter's thatch of hair,
thin flake of the moon, a creamy dust.

Their right hand itches, and the juice works
in their mouths. What invitations
to spill the beans, take lines for walks,
or post a statement to the nation,
blind Homer's eyes for a watermark

rough as justice, age-old, sore:
tablets for all the shapes and sizes
of wishes and wants edging round the door,
the artist's hurt, the model's poses,
the face that never lifts from the floor.

All four winds sough in the paper. Welcome
to their rich laurels and distresses.
Welcome to Tracy and Mnemosyne,
Hokusai's numberless addresses
sown like grain from a careless palm.

That girl will forever be flying her kite
over the rooftop of youth
while some old duffer falls for art
and the standing committee on God's truth
stumbles into the failing light.

Flying to Agra

The waiters wore elaborate turbans
which somehow increased the sadness
of their pointed slippers and pantaloons,
emerging from Mount Rushmore faces
to extend the franchise of rice.

Chopin proved to be in the keeping
of the hotel's sixteen-year-old daughter
who joined me in the leafy swimming pool
at the bottom of the garden where
turbid water dozed off in the sun.

I was on hand to stage tourist arrivals
incontrovertibly in front of the Taj
and send them taxiing on to Delhi.
She held my hand in the cinema, tight,
keeping it well and truly joined

as the heroine raised her larynx
over the sub-continent. Then billiards
at the club with the man who sold me
a ruby ring. I impressed everyone
with the quality of my losing hazards,

learned from my father as a boy.
Chopin floated from the hotel verandah.
There was a dawn chorus like *Belshazzar's Feast.*
Back to the ship in Bombay in a sealed
compartment. I remembered a shabby bear

on a road, in chains. I remembered
the tree of vultures. I saw myself
seeing the Taj in all lights, and getting
my reflections right, and wishing we had
that tremendous palm-to-palm goodbye.

When they play a note they bend it
so it talks itself to silence, coming
back round the dark side of the wrist
while moonlight shivers all along
the water, and the sympathetic humans

vibrate with a long slow shake of the head.

Man and Woman at a Casement

Fra Filippo Lippi

As well they might be
hatted and head-dressed
with her level eye
imperiously loosed
at his more than glance,
the pleasant impertinence

called youth. There's just a slice
of his face, only greedy
for love. Summoned or lost
to the necessity
that's her? Unreadable,
therefore she's the tall

order of the luxurious two,
hands folded, calm, pale, rich
in presence, propriety,
virginal pearl necklace
warming to the deep red
stuff in which she's cosseted,

fair hair scraped back
under her elaborate
jewelled untouchable look
that calmly cries out
to be touched, despite
or because of her state

in the grand Florentine
order of things, where girls
turn women at thirteen,
consequently marriageable
at a price he may determine
with that bold looking-in.

Nowadays they would meet
at a party or a club,
she consciously bright
and me a bit glib
with my heavens above
looks worn on my sleeve,

my bibliographical thanks
for such grave princesses
as I got in the drinks
and warmed to existence's
mania for the scarlet
embrasures of thought.

Retrospective

Gwen John's women only just
make it onto the canvas. Pale blue's
the colour of the birth they choose
not to announce. They're fading fast

into a future of unreachable
addresses, high single bed,
cats, letters posted or unposted,
three or four cowslips on the table

murmuring of Ophelia's trailed coat,
one fork and spoon, devoutly crossed,
some sort of mirror, spotted with rust,
a knife-edge cameo at the throat.

Any minute now the master
will come hurrying in from the storm
with the tablets smoking under his arm—
the ultimate disaster.

On the run-up to my 49th birthday

Oh, but the hand that holds her breast is grassy!
—Brecht

Here's a black felt slipper on a foot
three parts submerged in sock
like Chairman Mao swimming down the Yellow River.

My stomach creeps outward
in a fine friendship with the earth
like Chairman Mao swimming down the Yellow River.

There is time on my hands, and a fat
lot of geography in my address book
like Chairman Mao swimming down the Yellow River.

Mother came to stay with her death inside her
making its way gradually out to us
like Chairman Mao swimming down the Yellow River.

In the handbag were lipstick and mirror
clacking against a comb with rounded teeth
like Chairman Mao swimming down the Yellow River.

I have renewed the cat, installed
a goldfish who does modern dance
like Chairman Mao swimming down the Yellow River.

It's a long march, a long swim.
You'd never believe it. These feet have seen
Chairman Mao swimming down the Yellow River.

Holding the Surface

'Just listen to this,' you say, deep
into the words of your favourite
as we sit with the wounded envelopes
of the morning post, and the coffee pot.

This is a good time, round the table,
cherishing an unused day,
you with your specs, Platonic owl
consulting the book across your knee

and me not listening, because I want
out of the babble of other men's art,
to carry my lusciously silent tongue
upstairs, to a quiet place apart.

And this annoys you, that time and again
I'm full of me, like a jug of cream
reserved for a corner table of one
that won't be poured till kingdom come.

But it isn't that. I like the peaceful
tilt of you, head, book, and cup.
I like the light along the table
holding the surface to its lip.

The green blind stirs. Pale sun slants in,
the handle of your lightest brush,
loading our Dutch-quotidian
exactly as a granted wish.

Inventions

i.m. Norman Nicholson, 1914-1987

1.
There are lakes in our region
        small English lakes
with even smaller islands floating in them
        holding a dark stand of trees.

Only the very luckiest roots
        get taken on there.

2.
All down the coast old factories
        revert to soil and scrub.
It doesn't take much to heave off
        raw industrial brick.
But these old trees are tough. They bow
        to no-one but themselves.

3.
Water hammers on the beach,
        dimples in the lake,
it holds up its dress this way
        and that way in the beck.

There floats the island
        which is a fist of earth
or an invention of the mind.

Just one step, it says,
        just one more step
and either the world will open
        or it will have dodged back
into your pocket, like a coin.

4.
I was late for your funeral, Norman.
The wind blew against me, the car
        slowed, three Herdwicks skittered
on the narrow Thirlmere road.
        It seemed to take forever to get round
and round to your spit of land.

I came back by the coast under Black Combe,
        thus making of it a round trip.
The June fields grew a yellowish grass,
        that shade old Faber covers
fade to, when a book was a real book.

Faces

Those Slav faces
are hollowed flints, striking fire
in the back of the cave. Or a thin ice
of counts and princes
clashing gently under the chandelier.

They will address
themselves only to man's fate,
the woman question, farming, how to bless
affairs of heart and of the state
with godliness,

that tender howl
of aspiration, torn straight from the beast's back
and thrown across superfluous man
whose shivering soul
craves warmth and reason.

They had messages
for the world, or so they thought,
which ran to love, forgiveness, holy fools
in many thousand pages
few could read, and fewer bought;

nobles and peasants
in a dream of peace, a panacea
devoutly to be wished,
as one class got itself a big idea
and the other washed.

See Dostoyevsky
declaiming at the statue's foot,
the open-mouthed world proletariat
marching along Nevsky
chanting for writers to be shot.

The big, big tune
deep thinkers were to teach the west
went flat. Tchaikovsky beat his spacious breast.
The dying swan
tipped under. Yet the violin

persists, wants
'something higher' counted among
our small denominations (as we fence
the infill sites
for one more shopping precinct):

which has to do
with something lower, kindliness
for instance, paddling its wares like ducks and drakes
in search of food
and warmth on winter lakes.

Relatively
few of the old absolutes
survive flea markets and the heightened brow,
save those fur hats
whose faces face the music now,

high cheeks still tart
as Cubist paintings, bearing down
on Red Square's crate
of upturned faces, forever asking
that old burning question

conscience can't shrug off
with Stateside orthodontics, politesse
sub-Windsor style, French elegance,
while the great bell of Kiev
booms out its bronze defiance . . .

faces you could
split the atom with, or get drunk
with, dive into vowels deep as tidal pools,
come up for air with a mad monk
or Gogol's fools

then hibernate
with loveable Oblomov, who
can't be fussed with madam's *érotique*
and patent leather shoe
while there's a pillow for his neck—

the neck Ras-
kolnikov took an axe to, in
another context. The Russian thought-police
are tireless,
both for good and ill. That pain,

that nameless pain
existence on a blowy day
pinned to your chest,
is it of the highest, the very best,
or just a speck the wind will blow away?

Neighbours

If God had meant us to settle in communes
or move in next to our best friends He
would never have invented La Rochefoucauld
and games of chance, the yale lock, the ingle
nook, telephones, the dog's incessant itch to bark
first and wag later. It would be like living
on muesli or monads, doing ourselves nothing
but good, which is a destructive scenario.

Look at the Bloomsberries, kissing and calling,
in and out of each other's pockets like billiard balls,
or the Tolstoyans who moved in high above Slad
in their pacific sandals and tiny wood houses
after the Great War, setting their feet down
thoughtfully on the scarp. Intellectual consanguinity
is deficient in roughage. You can landscape a
landscape, knowing full well that summer's grand slam
will defeat you, but human engineering is always
a mistake. Witness the slums of Bogotá, the breeding
techniques of royalty—all those pearly vowels
strung out on threadbare genes. No wonder they
slammed doors of the pyramids tight shut.

Better to bow to the gods of rough justice
who put up this street and hid its deep grammar
from all but those who whistle on ladders
and grow their own jam. The highest merit lies
in the slightly-oiled salesman, the solicitor's Volvo,
its sidelights' eternal flame, the diurnal jingles
of the fish-van coaxing a widow out of purdah
to set the brass weights moving on cold scales.

Bad luck to the school of like minds
if they don't break a mental leg somewhere
on this terrain, which is rough as a bed
of oysters, crusted with pure contingency.
Strange forms of life live on the backs

and fronts of our neighbours, salutary
fronds, retributive mandibles, innumerable modes
of ingestion and digestion, whose consciousness
raises and lowers itself. This is the great
good place, the watering-hole, the sparrow-jump
where moss colonises the roof-slates, tomatoes
giggle on window-sills, soot grows up the chimney
like a larch, and at supper everyone eats right down
to the lovers on their bridge of sighs.

Through Glass

To Ben on his 21st birthday

You came too soon. We had no money then.
No sense either. The flat was cramped and small.
Books, pictures, egos littered every wall.
A rubber plant stood in for England's Eden.
Students, we thought the sun would never set
on the crown of our first mushroom omelette.

You came too soon, lighter by several pounds
than textbook babies were supposed to be,
and lay there in a capsule nursery
with tubes and flexes monitoring your wounds,
as though the journey had exhausted all
your powers of being. Young but stoical

the three of us began to learn to live
and you were slowly nurtured, under glass,
instead of sprawling at your mother's breast
which ached with all the love she had to give.
It beamed in through the unit, through the trees,
powering the tigers on the nursery frieze.

We broke the glass at last, and took you home,
and laid you down among superfluous toys
whose colours were another burst of sunrise.
You seemed quite comfortable with your fame,
yawned once or twice, practised a newly deep
uncomprehending stare, and fell asleep.

So then we lived by weights, clocks, temperatures,
the inside of the wrist, a holy spot
most apt to speak of our unending plot
to fatten up your poles and hemispheres.
Your eyes swam so far up into your head
I thought you'd drowned, and all aboard were dead,

capsized in this niagara of warm milk . . .
But no, you'd just elected to drift off
and sway suspended like a piece of kelp,
leaving behind an odoriferous burp
that said, in cartoon bubbles, Just a tick.
Don't go away, you two, I'll soon be back!

I strolled the lovely squares and terraces
where Clifton falls away, like Babylon,
into the arms of Hotwells, and the Avon
winds through gorges that it never muddies,
though smells of slavery still hang about
the Grand Hotel's old kitchen porter's light.

What was I wedded to? Ah that, that was
the question. Where did Hamlet and my wife
debate the mephistophelean terms of life;
and what was marriage anyway, to cause
such daily ructions as disturbed the peace
of married folk, in 1966?

Royal York Crescent put its balconies,
its flagstones, railings, sweetly curving mind,
its airy rooms, with boards of polished sand,
at the beck and call of student reveries.
Many a hand went to a noble brow
and dropped no whit the wiser. Anyhow

you looked at it love in the books was not
quite on all fours with us, whose little trick
of running ourselves ragged was the *ding an sich*
both Kant and Buddha took their potshots at
from comfortable distances, secure
in their exact, regressive sinecure.

Reason, I gradually came to think,
is the most battered wife there ever was,
clipped and confined in bogus essences,
abused by every genius and crank
who says he likes this bit of her, or that,
and claps the rest beneath his foolish hat.

28

The wrong time is the one precisely right.
Who'd touch a lip to order, save up hard
and calculate the life they can afford?
Or bow to logic, wisdom? Legislate
a narrowing of mind, to fit in thought
between the ears of Plato, or Descartes?

I cannot like those childless couples who
brush specks of dust off coffee tables, books,
arrange their magazines in wooden racks,
write up a diary, play at peekaboo
at dinner parties, concerts, therapists,
and waft deep fragrances on dainty wrists.

In labs, in libraries, in honeycombs
where queen bees of the intellect loll at ease
there are exact equivalents of these
polishing up their matchless theorems,
whose progeny are footnotes, born to sting
marauding facts to death as they fly in.

Item: each maker is an autocrat
in thrall to hierarchies of common sense.
Item: instinct is its own recompense.
Item: pure mess and muddle is the cat
who licks the cream, purrs *Quis custodiat?*
Item: art or life in the bassinet?

Some such inarticulate bellyache
rested, oh Ben, upon your coming here,
the melancholy, long withdrawing roar
of my commitment to life for art's sake.
Whereof I could not speak, I thought that brains
would scour the murky stuff out of my veins.

So nursing you on one arm, nursing me,
my marriage, and my studies on the other,
tiptoeing round *Tractatus* and the weather
that blows through every new-born family
I hatched out parlous footnotes on To be . . .
brooding on love's responsibility.

All parents are beginners, *faute de mieux*.
You practise on the first one. No-one knows
what they most need to, or where knowledge grows.
The curse or cry that first comes echoing through
delivery rooms is the divining call
peculiar to this bare, forked animal

and who or where it comes from, what it plumbs
or points to, is anybody's guess,
and so, between the starlight and the grass,
we suck opposable, intellectual thumbs
as if, by *Philosophical Investigations*,
we'd hush that noise, and all the noise of nations.

Clifton Bridge arched over the abyss.
The camera obscura gentled all:
all dreamlike, sad, and wholly beautiful,
heartbreaking woods, the gloomy haunts of Dis,
rust on the leaves, a swift Homeric gleam
lighting the knife-edge of that placid stream.

Just there, where mind is dumb, was our good place
and yours . . . weighed in at nothing very much.
Your infant diet was impossibly rich,
your parents barely of the human race
up in that eyrie, balanced on a shout
I still can't fathom, till I write it out

or try to, and grow dizzy with my lust
to lay the ghost of error, fasten names
dispassionate as moss that slowly swims
across the gouged-out lettering of the past
on the unnameable, that fell from space
to earth, bearing its name upon your face.

The Emperor of China

after Heine

My father was a dry old stick,
a martyr to angina
but me, I wet my lips, and I'm
the Emperor of China.

It has green fingers, my sweet schnapps,
it sows a wild perfume
and when I look into my mind
all China is in bloom!

The swamps dry out, the peasants turn
to happy nymphs and gentle swains.
One glance from me, my wife swells up
melodiously with labour pains.

The sick take up their beds and walk.
The civil service goes to work.
All error dies. Peace takes root.
The PM budgets on his flute.

Asparagus instead of rice
is what my people eat.
The pingpong fans dance on the green
by two and two, with nimble feet.

And palace mandarins file out
to smile a meum, tuum,
pigtails flying roundabout
the Heavenly Bicycle Museum.

All the temples fill with souls,
with incense, and with prophecies;
bandits take up begging bowls;
the Jews convert, on bended knees.

Then all the bigwigs vote themselves
out of a job, for love of China.
Rule over us, you poets, rule
flat out, like Heinrich Heine!

*

I drink too much, the doctor says.
Much he knows, of words or wine.
Here's a health, a Marseillaise
in mandarin. This empire's mine!

North

'I'll tell you, that being passed through Highgate, there
I was saluted by the country air . . .
And (which I'm sure you long to know) set forth
In Northern song my journey to the North'
                              —Charles Cotton, 'Epistle to John Bradshaw, Esq'

Three hundred and thirty years ago, it took
        the northern bard and part-time rake
four days, and heaven knows how many horses,
        pints and pies and coachman's curses,
to shift himself upcountry, landing where
        the Dove hems rocky Staffordshire.

Bucking and bouncing up the motorway
        we do it now in half a day
dodging between the artics and the laws
        like nifty pilots in Star Wars
one eye out for the cops, and one on dials
        monitoring our fancy wheels

while Mozart, handy-packed onto a tape,
        carves time into sonata-shape
and all the Domesday census rushes by
        in micro-twinklings of an eye
which rests, unresting, on a hawk that stalls
        above the mole's blue overalls.

Once there, in Peak, or Dale, or Fell, wherever
        the hills accelerate a river
and Mother offers up into the skies
        her breastwork of allegories
I cut the engine, shut the terrace door,
'The same dull Northern clod I was before.'

In my case, Charles, there's money to be earned
        and, inbetween, my fingers burned
on vernal beauties, or big-city poems
        innocent of country iambs
which someone wants me to review—a foxy
        raid on subtexts, done by proxy.

It doesn't make you friends, or earn much grub,
        or kudos in the Groucho Club
where, I imagine, young and midlife turks
        work out the status of their Works
by simple divination: who's with whom,
        ascendant in the Starlight Room.

The provinces—Dutch paintings, English books,
        French architecture, and French cooks,
Greek nonchalance with marble, German fugues,
        Southern Comfort, Irish brogues—
are nine-tenths of the body politic,
        whether the body's well or sick.

So let the capitals rave on: they're built
        for pleasure, throwing out ideas.
And let the sodium lamps forever halt
        the far side of this vale of tears
where greeny thoughts reach down into the clay
        and glimmer there, to live or die.

The latest cosmological hunch
        is that the world is out to lunch
for free. Something came out of nothing, sprang
        all matter from the void, in a Big Bang
which bent the laws of physics, giving us
        a ghostly glimpse of Genesis . . .

Mirror speaks unto mirror, as it can:
    a quantum leap from space to man
who holds the memory of nothingness
    as close, Charles, as the natal mess
of parturition, and the traveller's code
    for getting up the Great North Road.

Your politics aren't mine; yet we'd agree
    precisely nothing is for free—
not physics, metaphysics, roundheads, square,
    young fogeys, old ones, clodhop, squire;
not dithyrambs, to turn a lovely head,
    nor quarks, with bony wrists outspread.

Today the snow came down, to left and right,
    rhyming with everything in sight.
Each flake was eloquent. I left my words
    to scatter bread for freezing birds
and what the text was that we made, or were,
    was written on that bolt of air.

Accident

The siren's thin blue alp of sound
looms up, and fades, on city streets.
An angel's fallen to the ground
bleeding in a hail of lights.

Its long, accusing finger sweeps
round asphalt, concrete, stony spire,
the unaccommodating face
to face of earth and air and fire.

Excitement glows, then, turning away
the crowd burns off in twos and threes,
is gone. The angel's here to stay,
beating its wings behind the eyes.

Trains

1
If ever there was a vehicle for nostalgia

2
Puffing along between heaven and earth

3
There is the carriage of childhood

4
The interview that will dig up your days

5
No such thing as an undecided train

6
Throbbing and slowing. Full tilt. Inch by inch

7
Ears eyes nose hands tongue

8
There is terror of stepping on the wrong train

9
Terror of stepping on the only train

One Man

A block of flats, somewhere in Turin.
A stairwell, neither here nor there, anonymous
as scuff-marks wrappers buttons echoes.
It is the spiral steps are mounted in
with iron uprights, shabby at the knees,
a rail to haul on, bleak infinities

of doors and doorways, opened just a crack.
Warm air blurts out, to tangle in the hall
with blasts of cold. It sees a body fall
through bony floors, then spider on its back.
The telex throbs, spitting its letters home.
Implacable chatter at the gates of Rome.

Primo Levi's dead. One man has gone
back down alone, to circle endless fire.
Stigmata of pure reason and barbed wire,
whose corpus is the earth he walked upon,
receive, bind, mortify this blessed ghost,
laid down among the shadows he engrossed.

Some lines of Dante haunted him, compounded by
tormenting gaps. The dull cadavers sang
in broken words, while mothers deftly hung
out children's clothing on barbed wire to dry.
It flaps there still, the only way it can.
Clean air blows through it, moving like a tongue.

Tristia

after Mandelstam

I've studied hard to learn to say goodbye,
a word that grows enormous in the throat
like saplings looming up towards the sky
on summer nights, towards a balm of light
that sets the ox-jaw moving, and a cry
split harshly from the cockerel on the dump
as naturally as tears enlarge an eye
brushed softly by the halo of a lamp.

What nourishment is there in speech? 'Apart'
will part us, surely as the cockerel crows,
planting its arbitrary plosives in the heart.
Old fires on the Acropolis will blaze
new meaning out across wide city streets
heralding the dawn of some new age
while oxen lower heads, to grind up roots,
and roosters beat their wings in joyful rage.

Meanwhile I contemplate the love I have
for those swift crepitations of the loom,
the spindle humming like a thing alive
and shuttles fluttering out their solid flame.
The shreds are flying: all the bits of words,
the tiny wastages, the happiness
we might have woven, lovely as the braids
a woman shakes out to an oaken tress

are lost. They will be found, and lost again,
for divination, like a well-loved hymn,
is sacred to the earth; it will go on
singing from Hellas to Byzantium.
It's not for us to ponder the Greek hell
of pitted bronze, devouring of the face
by women's fingers, shrieking as they tell
each bone's exact and final resting place.

Nobody

Nobody goes barefoot here
on wide-apart hips
at one or two hours per hour
netting the olives.

No jeep sweats round the hill
with a living to make
from fish, flesh or fowl
in amplified Greek.

Green grow the rushes,
rain, slugs, tearful roses,
all the origin of species.

Bounce off the walls. Buzz on the pane.
Fetch me a word, a dagger of sun.
Clytemnestra. Agamemnon.

The Charterhouse of Nab

What happens to Fabbrizio del Dongo
is lust, religion, love and war,
not necessarily in that order,
whirling round him in a latin tango.

I knew a Fabbio once. He went sailing
on Rydal Water, so good-looking
in his olive skin, his boxers, water dripping
from oiled pecs, his Sony Walkman drumming,

all the women at his language-school
forgot their verbs
and rushed to find a towel

good enough to dry off Fabs,
who'd fashion it sarong-wise, well
tucked in among that plethora of ribs.

From Pica to Mockba

The intellectual has a thousand reasons
why the case is complex, will not yield
to any of the senses or the seasons.
'Life is not a walk across a field'

says the old Russian proverb. Yet it is.
At least, the carefree poet told us so.
He preens a little, one eye on his feathers,
one on the modest bathos of his shoe . . .

or dives, like Byron, into the Grand Canal,
holding aloft a fiery, snatched flambeau
to light his way through Venice's warm swell
of church and palace, convent and bagnio.

He shakes his pelt. The marble darkens then,
mocking his ictus with a hollow shout.
Clean linen waits, a candle, and a pen.
One of his mistresses will wring him out.

Poem for a Younger Son

This one steps into an outsize pair of wings
and commits hubris that he lives to tell.
One minute a model of Epstein's rock drill,
padded and helmeted, the next he flings
his torso off the face of the fell

into strong creaky arms of wind
that dandles him up like a baby. There
all earth recedes to a miniature
of unperspectived, geometric land
and only the cloud-base sings in his ear.

I'm left behind, with an upturned face
and lurching heart, as he skates on air
then turns and mounts up, higher and higher,
waving (damn fool!) from the height of his bliss,
whirled out like the topmost spark of a fire.

And the blaze is kindled by all his years
as a last-born, follower, third man on the rope
oppressed by the company he must keep:
the oxygen of a mother's fears,
and father's rules, a tape with a loop.

No sage, no art-encrusted connoisseur
saw the Lakes like this; nor you and me.
The poet trusts only to metaphor
but the poet's son knows how to fly,
what inspiration is really for,

the code of the competent: lightly keep
skimming the silence, smile into your beer.
Words for the wordy, parsons for sheep,
and the rush of the angel nowhere, nowhere
but waking out of the family sleep.

The Harrowing of the North

1.
You never know what you'll be surprising
in the bottomless valleys of Durham—
whippets, American football, a round dozen
from the Poly quantifying boredom

among ex-miners hefting a wash
of crimson lake over
and above the rolling wave
of cartridge paper

thumb-tacked to a desk
in the Infants—bitter
at night—as teacher lass

gets skylines bled
of all that racket and clutter
where Consett once stood.

2.
Twelve miles as the rook
in *Macbeth* creaks off to the wood
lies the chemical dump at Siddick,
a short run from Sellafield.

Open-cast mines, subbed out *pro-tem*
by the NCB; and the soapy
works at Whitehaven
lathering half the Irish Sea.

A lonely tocsin sounds
out on the Solway:
fish out of bounds

here, lobsters kaput, gulls
nursing their grievance far away
inland, on dumps and spills.

3.
When the big new THORP plant comes onstream
in nineteen-ninety-something
we shall, the boffins say, be reckoning

up millisieverts of radioactive crackle
in fractions of the insouciant waffle
that once passed for safety. Piffle

is largely retroactive in this
industry, existing always and forever lost
in some British Standard Past Tense
of Nemesis,

otherwise known as not-in-the-public-
interest, right Simon? Let that
video unit get cracking quickly
and check the lettering on the doormat.

4.
The last pair of eagles in the north
mounts a round-the-clock watch
on a variegated batch
of anoraks tightening their girth

on the heritage industry:
shepherd's numerals for brunch, say,
then 'Carlisle . . . [O planner's fantasy]
Great Border City'

for tea. The twa corbies
have pecked out their messuage
from Millom to Dumfries:

gentrified pillage
fleece over fleece
village by village.

Dunmail Raise

On the day of the big snow
the Vale of Grasmere
swallowed hard and took a vow
of silence. Michael's sheep were
getting hard to find. Dove Cottage
(*née* the *Dove & Olive Bough*)
was turning whiter
than a whited sepulchre.
The lake froze solid, turning a blind eye.

Back at the Nab
the ghosts of Quince and Hartley
went on babbling, blab blab
glug. The Scar looked swell.
Helm Crag wore its plumage well
going nowhere in the grandest style.

Halfway up the Raise
my waggon skittered off and swerved
about in many ways
as though King Dunmail woke up, heaved
his chest, then looked off west
to crave a boon
and parley with his opposite number
over the water, Pat Mael Duin;
or, failing that, the poet Wordsworth
noted for his walking sideways
going boom boom boom.

It seemed that someone was anxious
to influence my way home,
so there I was among the giants
facing back the way I'd come.

The old isolation ward on the tops
is feverish now with anoraks,
crampons, pitons, ice-picks, all
the stuff that's really off the wall,

searching out dark spots of time
for the gospel of the ultimate climb.
Three hefty lads, three Michelin men
whose stubble was a quickset hedge,
all set to saunter up Helvellyn
and cartwheel back down Striding Edge
soon got me on my travels again

and me and the car
rowed slowly up the length of Thirlmere
(past the rock that Rawnsley pinched
from the Water Board of Manchester,
for several parties had once inched
certain initial letters there)
and on down the valley, still in thrall
to the several billion tons of snow
sparkling all over St John's in the Vale,
nowhere more than on Castle Rock
whose lineaments once gratified
the big bow-wow of Sir Walter Scott;
where one cold midnight De Quincey rather
fancied he saw a frosty moon-bather
flat on his back in the middle of the week
and wisely decided not to speak . . .

And so into Keswick, by Shelley's cottage,
round past the school where the anthill was—
Aunts Southey and Lovell and Coleridge—
and everybody was dearest coz
until they grew up, and could hear no more
the merry, merry minstrelsy
of the fading, falling Falls of Lodore
or the hunger pangs of Papa Bear
honeying the nursery . . .
and Sam's great view of Borrowdale
was borrowed only to see him fail.

There goes my road
on past the master's *Dejection Ode*,
round by Crosthwaite's paean of trees

where Southey is parked on his hands and knees
north by west of the sturdy nave
in a protestant—Brazilian grave.

The fine new road goes broad and straight
(straight and broad the road goes on)
along the margins of Bassenthwaite
where Skiddaw keeps a friendly eye on
the Mirehouse literary lion

and the arm that reaches up for the sword
out of the bosom of the mere
belongs to the Lake District Tourist Board
chaired by Hon Sir Bedivere

and so, past Cockermouth's castle walls
where ghosts are said to walk at night
through town to my not quite marble halls
though the TV could be mystic samite . . .

(Both the dogs began to howl.
I thought at first I'd lost my yale
but it was safe, foregrounded in
Cole's Notes to *The Advancement of Learning*.)

There on the screen a young man makes
fresh copy out of *The Land of the Lakes*,
humping his cables, mikes and masses
of fully-frontal Claude glasses
in which you can see, look! clear as a whistle
old Dunmail turning into Ken Russell
brandishing his Panaflex
at mother nature's teeming sex,
the spontaneous overflow of nipple,
delta, omega, omphalos,
or what you will, or deep chiasmus.
'Cut!' he roars, 'It's in the can'

and dies back down
beneath his desecrated cairn—
the one they moved to build a road
might help you up it when it snowed—
that no-one scratched initials on.

Cradle Song

The sirens wailed: crowds of shadows fled
far down into the darkness, pressed together
as though to wall the living from the dead.

My cradle, mother told me, was a leather
bag, or soap box, rocked upon her knee
while voices rose and fell for hours together,

straining to catch the movements of a sky
gone dark, a waypath for unfriendly wings
that brushed all earth awake. Including me,

she said; for though they sang me all the nothings
in the book, soothed and rocked me all night long,
I slept no more than their imaginings—

a babe all blissful on the wings of song—
or summer curlews; and looked up at them
as wide awake as mother's wedding ring.

Yesterday, when rain had streaked the car
with little bombs of dust, I thought how weird
that skies should rain down dirt, and freshen fear

they laid to rest with thermoses and cards,
old shapeless overcoats, thick socks, a scree
of neighbours, fast asleep on wooden boards,

and that first disobedience of the eye.

Green Over Blue

The village by the sea
was deadly boring to a boy
for waves struck at the pier
only because the pier was there
and great liners sailed
off to encounter the world

leaving their agitated wash
fraying the shallows of the beach
where seagulls muscled in
on a dead salmon
bruised quiet as mud, then
clapped off screeching

like baptists. The second coming
if there was to be one
took the form of wave or leaf
or swimmable New Forest
streams, a fallen log across
that clear and meditative face.

What can be done with a tree
but climb it? And a rusty yew
that won't turn into Robin's bow
or bend across a naked knee,
with hazel arrows, hard to fledge,
cut green and perfect from the hedge?

Old Fraser had barbed-wire
tweeds, club tie, an arctic glare
all week. His short black cane
barked even the hardest palm.
You weren't to shout. On poppy day
he wore his medals. Penelope

Young, the robin of our class,
God gave to smile at me at last.
She offered up her face. I bit
a portion from her apple cheek
and chewed it half a lifetime, till
I'm grown around that secret smile—

the russet and the leaf that hides
its growing. Still the waves
lap at me. If not sea it was
the Cotswolds, or the northern fells,
for cities rose and fell in a flash
and my flesh was somehow grass

imprinted with that village hue:
in either case, green over blue
chasing each other, as the weight
of tides broke on the Isle of Wight
or shadows of low jets were thrown
like tomahawks across Old Man.

Love in a mist, love's origin
in sudden hapless parenting—
what grey roof or pavement could
assuage a heart, as well as mud?
I've circled all the globe, I've
known the rich, and grown a slave,

pitched my tent in New York's glare,
been to Japan, been everywhere
that offered spells to educate
a stubborn mind, a backward heart
lost now to all but that low roar
in wind, the sea upon the shore.

Downpipes

after Novella Matveyeva

Straight as arms
down a soldier's blouse
the downpipes stand
on every house,
black and mouldy,
furred with moss,
old mouths gossiping
of pain and loss.

The rain trickles out
through iron joints
and the rusty old spout
sputters and talks,
whispering secrets,
a winter's tale
of cracked regrets
blurted out to a fool.

Yes, I believe you.
Behind this wall
there was lies, suffering,
inconceivable
dearth, stray kindness
shuffling its clogs,
a cold slow damp
on kitchen flags.

Shut up, can't you?
We don't want to hear
that endless rehearsal,
canonical blur
fogging the entry,
choking up drains.
We're young. We'll make up
our own tunes.

Drips galore.
Stone slimed and green.
Never a silence.
The rain ticks down
and you must utter
your pebble of truth
sucked smooth as time
in an open mouth.

Stare at the Moon

'One day a young English poet will write a sonnet to it'—*The Observer* on Charles Johnston's translation of *Eugene Onegin*.

'Literature is the folklore of the educated'—Louis Simpson.

I'm not so young, but I'll oblige,
and in the master's stanza too.
Shakespeare made it all the rage.
Byron packed it in his shoe.
In Milton's and in Wordsworth's hands
it thundered in upon the sands
of being. Hopkins made it weep
for his sad self. Donne made it deep.
Yeats climbed aboard the shuttle, Keats,
and soared off into the sublime.
Owen worked in pararhyme
clipping the wings of Paracletes.
So master-spirits raise up storms
by conjuring the form of forms.

That's quite enough by way of proem.
I come to raise my English hat
to Pushkin, and to Pushkin's poem,
translated by a diplomat—
who else?—presenting his credentials
at the court of bare essentials,
youth, love, tears, art, dreams, space, time
housed in a palace built of rhyme—
theme of many a turgid lecture!
I'd rather weave a circle, thrice,
and point you at their joint device,
this miracle of architecture
floating on cyrillic stems
where Neva meets the river Thames.

Eugene's Childe Harold, in a huff,
a moody Dane, young Lochinvar.
And Tanya's all the dreamy stuff
that ever swung upon a star.
His pain is mine. Her guileless art
has stamped its foot upon my heart.
Who has not perished in the fire
of Russia's prose, 'proud Albion's lyre,'
deconstructed through and through
then put together, whole again,
by red blood flowing through a pen
that stains a wilderness of snow?
Inspired, we rush to man the plough
of our own story, anyhow

so long as breath breathes us a word,
so long as, in this middle way,
we take our flight—matchless, absurd—
thorough the woods of DNA.
With Keats's blush, and Marlowe's strut,
and Rilke's throne of angels (but
instantiated, made anew
for more than just a solemn few),
let's meet halfway, as best we can,
the author, authorising us
to write him a tumultuous
rewording of his godlike plan,
namer of names! lord of all lust!
yet shy of men, and dry as dust.

My Tatyana, mind and heart,
has come in three quite different styles.
To catch the throb of her least part
I'd need Donne's skills, or Raphael's.
I'll tell you this, though. Each possessed
within that holy source, the breast,
those qualities we're loth to praise
since theorists mended our ways.
Put to the question, what poor male
would pass the test, with his belief

that woman has a higher brief,
the word made flesh, and flesh made whole,
an ever-loving spring of tact,
while men froth up with 'truth' and 'fact'?

I know it's sentimental to
impute to one sex all the good
or bad. I know that quite a few
are witches, wodwos. If I could
I'd vote myself a spell of years
among my women friends and peers
as one of them, see how it feels
to wear men's fictions at my heels;
try out Diana's looks and brains,
read books with Lyn, climb high with Jan
among the torrents of Old Man,
squeeze both my hips in Olive's jeans,
go ape with Liz, oracular
in pre-Socratic Greek, with Fleur.

Or then again with Tanya, wide-
eyed,waiting all this time for me
to fall off Rosinante's hide
and get down to real history.
My Tanya, that is, pianist
and painter; next, biologist
who spoke in flowers, and dreamed in song
four preternatural summers long;
and then the other, girl-gazelle,
born to sniff the mountain air
and shake out her great mane of hair
along the ridges of the fell.
Each had a plethora of means.
One day I'll write *A Book of Genes*,

a treatise on the wrist, the neck,
bare legs and arms, the creases, motes
of hairs and moles and goldenfleck
seeding themselves on backs and throats.
These have their analogues in thought.

That's why the spirit is so fraught,
so torn between the soviet
of bodies, instinct's A to *stet*,
and reason's lonely, selfish pride
which doubts that it's worthwhile to take
a header in the lovers' lake
and contradiction in its stride.
What can't be found, and won't be lost,
and haunts us still: our holy ghost.

My good intentions, see, are fine.
Like yours, no doubt. But in the end
we toe the atavistic line
of fearful love, make do and mend
what's past all mending. Keats's blush,
pure native sunrise of the flesh,
redeems, in part, a world gone dark,
the lower decks of Noah's ark
where instincts are all elemental.
Lesson one: adapt or die.
We're into that, that livid sky
at once indifferent, sacramental.
Blue globe, white cloud, spores, orts and speech.
Onegin, dumb, patrols the beach:

'culture, so far from healing, hurts us.'
What a line . . . Yet worth a thought.
(The context's manners; Russia versus
western decadence.) He brought
a well-stocked mind to bear, he looks
Romanticism's master-books
full in the face, and finds them bare
of sound and sense, full of hot air.
Alexander, it takes one to . . .
er . . . know one, if you get my drift.
Liberty stood there in her shift
stirred more than discontent in you.
Your gentle scoff at liberalism
in art and love's a Russian schism

detectable both then and now.
We have a version of it here.
Some see the stars. Some see the plough.
The prudent cit still cocks an ear.
Aesthetics into politics
won't go, for all the dirty tricks
department does its level best.
And yet this nice empiricist
deduction—'spheres of influence'—
means Leonardo's, Mozart's sense
never yet unclenched a fist;
and likewise that the artist's will
is no more than a weekend skill.

Questions go up into the air
quite literally. Think how a voice
when asking, sounding, rapt in prayer
curves up and out to empty space;
and how the voice goes heavy, flat,
puts on lead sinkers and a hat
and plods along the ocean floor
when bible-wise and certain-sure.
We need more one, they need more other.
Never did contraries so stand
in need of fruitful, common land
as *L'art pour l'art*, artless Big Brother.
Perhaps they'll meet, as opposites do,
when Hegel stoops to tie his shoe.

' . . . Only in January the snow,
night of the second, starting flaking.'
My birthday, reader. Pushkin knew
right about then I'd soon be waking,
Year of Our Lord One Nine Three Nine.
The continental world was shaking
as Hitler marched across the Rhine.
Sad dupes, and governments, were quaking.
More soldiers fed the Maginot Line.
The hands of Chamberlain were faking
peace, on paper. Peace would be fine,

Great Britain's for the simple taking
if only words meant what they say.
If not, then more than words would die.

Buzz-bombs doodled a stopping path.
Into the shelter for hours and hours.
I grew up in the aftermath
of the burning of the topless towers.
London, Coventry, Plymouth . . . The rule
was 'Do as you're told,' at home and school
'Grin and bear it.' 'It could be worse.'
Backs to the wall, then into the hearse.
In my house all the thirties meant
was men on the street, men at war,
fighting they hardly knew what for
one or another government.
The blitz spelled out our future in
the ABC of socialism.

Basta. I'm not about to mount
the scaffold of my life and times,
or give a full and frank account
of childish games and adult crimes.
Pace Wordsworth, they're all one;
the child who reels by wood and stone
mimicking owls' tremulous cry
calls down the fact that he must die.
Poet, soldier, thinker, meet
in burning forests of the night.
Club-fisted Keats adored to fight.
Kit Marlowe was so indiscreet
in doubting all the rules of men
he rushed upon a sharpened pen.

Evgeny didn't rush at all
and when he did it was too late.
One minute, cold and cynical,
the next despairing, desolate;
pierced by the simple verb 'to know,'
this schizophrenic to and fro

between repulsion and attraction,
body's pull, reason's detraction,
half-Lensky, half-Onegin, half
a roué, half an innocent,
half-black, half-white, half-penitent
(and wholly his own predicament)
he writes his final epitaph
in red, on snow—such a neat symbol!—
the universal calling card
of the Great Bear, serf, master, bard,
staking all on one last gamble;
Russian boor, Russian sublime
met in one Holy Russian rhyme.

The props are gone. The stage is stark.
'Post-modern' now, post-everything
that set a golden bird to sing
or Pushkin blazing in the dark.
But underneath we're just the same
whatever sort of fancy name—
Le Néant, Anger, Alienation—
upholsters our old desperation.
From boredom we too run a mile.
We pick and choose, call out a style
in sex, in money, school and church,
in science, and so-called research.
Hence my three Tanyas, my poor reach-
me-down Onegin, dropping names.
I simmer nicely in the flames
of brazen parts and dull pastiche.

Et in arcadia ego, says
the runic madman, strong and tall,
fixated on such cadences;
I want it now, I want it all,
every one of this world's goods,
'the total ownership of woods,'
wind and wave and woman-weather,
verse and prose, thrown all together.
That's our story, that's the game,

micro-, macro-, mucho. Riddle
me Lord of Hosts, the Cat and Fiddle,
cyrillic, English, all the same.
Author! Author! Where's Eugene?
What does your poem really mean?

Like *Godot*, nothing happens much.
Love doesn't get to coincide
with her and him. It loses touch
so there's no husband, no sweet bride.
When one is ready, t'other's not.
They fail to consummate the plot—
much as the couplet's searching feet
would stumble, if left incomplete.
It's nothing much. It's life and death.
It's tragic. Magic. Trumpery.
It's Russia's true obituary.
It's genius. A waste of breath.
PUSHKIN: one syllable to sigh
and one of bronze, to govern by.

How is it that the honest man
is lured by death, and hands that sigh,
must set his deepest wish to scan
those ancient windows in the eye?
Is moved by beauty, overmuch,
that writhes away beneath his touch?
The foot once set into a pool
treads leaf and sky under its heel.
One brilliant evening in mid-June
the fells burned in the western sun
so close, it seemed, a man could run
his fingers lightly down their spine.
Larks skelping upwards, into flight.
The cottongrass spread meekly white

across the marsh, laying a cloth
below its ancient lord, the hill.
We trod our own spontaneous path
up to the top. The air was still

62

as ever it is, as my son was
bounding on ahead because
perfection lay on each next crest,
the Solway blazing to our west,
the big fells, moon-bare, palm of rock
thrust upwards to a wash of sky
as startling as a Hokusai,
threw time and matter swiftly back
into the mind. The larks sang on
relentless as a singing stone.

Will Tanya meet Eugene again
one day, and fix him with a look
that heals up all their mutual pain
in those blank leaves that close a book?
Can he outwit his crazy mind
and seize a moment to be kind,
let go his bony grip on truth,
relax into the art of youth?
If not, we'll have to do it for them
with 'The Kiss', or *War and Peace*.
Eugene, you've been superfluous
quite long enough; now show decorum.
And, Tanya, no more flying kites.
The reader wants his common rights.

One man per girl, one girl per man.
One hearth, one home, one bed and board.
Byron finagles as he can—
the rules are different for a Lord.
If you two can't find out a cure
where's the use of literature?
The rain will set in, airs that kill.
I'll have to walk back down that hill
of happy endings, into life,
whose ragged textuality
speaks volumes as I turn the key,
the rhyme, the page, the door, the knife,
brush words aside, stare at the moon.
The cover's closed. I'm on my own.

Malcolm Lynch won  _Streets of Ancoats_, his varied career that inclu radium technician, fl carriage cleaner, and o many short stories and several radio plays, most of his work has been for television – including a year as editor of _Coronation Street_, as well as writing for _Crossroads_ and _Emmerdale Farm_. His film about building the QE2 on Clydebank for Scottish TV won an Emmy placing. In 1972 he was appointed executive editor of _The Archers_, at that time threatened with extinction: his brief was to update the series and inject it with realism and drama. More recently he was Newspaper Editor of the _Teignmouth Post_ in Devon. He is now retired and writing books.

The Streets of Ancoats is written out of his personal experience of childhood in that ghetto.

MALCOLM LYNCH

The Streets of Ancoats

Futura

A Futura Book

Copyright © 1985 by Malcolm Lynch

First published in Great Britain in 1985
by Constable and Company Limited, London

This edition published in 1989
by Futura Publications, a Division of
Macdonald & Co (Publishers) Ltd
London & Sydney

*All characters in this publication are fictitious
and any resemblance to real persons, living or dead,
is purely coincidental.*

All rights reserved
No part of this publication may be reproduced,
stored in a retrieval system, or transmitted, in any
form or by any means without the prior permission
in writing of the publisher, nor be otherwise
circulated in any form of binding or cover other
than that in which it is published and without a
similar condition including this condition being
imposed on the subsequent purchaser.

ISBN 0 7088 4311 5

Printed and bound in Great Britain by
Collins, Glasgow

Futura Publications
A Division of
Macdonald & Co (Publishers) Ltd
66–73 Shoe Lane
London EC4P 4AB

A member of Maxwell Pergamon Publishing Corporation plc

To the University of Manchester

Author's note

In the late 1920s Ancoats, Manchester, was one of the worst slums in Europe. Within an area of less than a square mile, squeezed between the middle of the city and the railway yards, lived about 30,000 people in black pigsty houses built during the Industrial Revolution. The houses were two up, two down, with just one cold water tap under the backyard window. Some of the streets were barely twelve feet wide. The average number of men, women and children living in these decaying hovels was said to be about six. Most of them were Irish and Italian immigrants.

It was barely ten years since the end of the Great War to save civilization. The heroes had been allowed to keep the greatcoats they'd worn in the trenches, and they still used them. The coats became bedding at night. Sick children, and there were many of them, were kept warm under these rotting garments.

Surrounding the black, dismal houses loomed the great cotton mills with their huge chimneys reaching into the grey sky like black fingers of Satan. For variety, there were rubber works and chemical factories among the cotton mills. The sky was so dark with smoke that in summer the sun could be seen as a red ball; in winter the only light came from the gas lamps.

This was the landscape Laurence Lowry sketched when he was collecting rents in the area. Today he would be lost in Ancoats, for Ancoats has gone; indeed the view from the spot where Lowry once stood would now more likely inspire a Turner.

In the 1960s Manchester bulldozed it all down; schools, library, museum, University Settlement, tramp ward and work-house – everything. It has been grassed and planted with shrubs and young trees; the Pennines can be seen in the distance; it is to be known as the Medlock Valley Park.

And the people? Where are the children of the people Lowry saw only as shabby matchstalk men, women and kids? Many are holding good jobs and living in the suburbs of the city; but the children of Ancoats can also be found in a Sydney bar, a

Melbourne department store, a restaurant in Toronto, a garage in Vancouver, a warehouse in Chicago, a police station in New York, a railway yard in Cape Town.

Frozen lavatories of winter

'Didn't she always think she was a cut above the rest of us? Taking the typewriting at night school!'

'And look where that's got her.'

The two old women were in a group of old women in shawls who stared at a house in Palmerston Street. They stood at a safe distance on the other side of the street and kept their eyes fixed on the bedroom window; for wasn't it in that very bedroom Kathleen Murphy was lying dead as a doornail, having taken her own immortal life by turning the gas tap on? And her being in the Children of Mary, at that!

That was about all Kevin and Patrick heard as they passed the group on their way to school. They glanced up at the window, but their minds were on other things. They were going to be tested on their catechism that very morning by Father Sullivan, and one moment of hesitation about why God made them and the old priest would belt them over the head with a prayerbook.

All they knew about Kathleen Murphy was that she had left school two years before. She worked at the Cleopatra Mill, but she wasn't a mill girl. She didn't open her curtains when the knocker-up tapped on the window; she didn't run down the street in clogs when the seven o'clock hooter blew; no shawl for her; she walked to the mill at half-past eight in a coat and hat. She worked in the office.

They had passed her house only last Saturday and heard her singing – 'For I'm in the market for you-oo-oo oo-oo. Boop-boop-a-doop!' She had strutted out of the house a few minutes later with circles of rouge on her cheeks and no shopping bag, which the boys had thought strange considering how she was supposed to be going to the market: their parents always took with them baskets which they filled with potatoes and cabbages found lying in the gutter after the market had closed.

There was no catechism that morning. Instead, Father Sullivan ranted and raved about the evil of suicide.

'The most precious gift God has given you is life. And if you

9

take away that life by your own hand then you are stealing from God what he has given you out of love. You will not be buried in consecrated ground waiting peacefully for the day of Resurrection. You will not be lifted up to heaven, for the Devil will already have taken your soul to be burned in everlasting hell fire.'

That night there was a knock on Kevin's door. It was Patrick, to ask if he was coming out to chase cats. But once outside Patrick confessed that chasing cats was only an excuse. He thought they could go and watch the house of Kathleen Murphy in case the Devil made an appearance at the window when he came to take her soul. He hadn't appeared yet, for the women had watched the house all day long, and they said nothing had happened, nothing at all.

The boys stared at the window so hard that even when they closed their eyes they could still see a red image of the window. But the Devil made no attempt to show himself. At one stage they began shouting 'Boop-boop-a-doop!' to remind the Devil where Kathleen Murphy was, in case he'd forgotten; but all that happened was a man came out from a house behind them and threatened to break their backs with a stair rod if they didn't shut up.

It wasn't a bit like other deaths they'd been to; for normally when somebody died the children would be invited in the house to look at the body and say a couple of Hail Marys, after which they'd be given a cup of ginger beer or American cream soda and an arrowroot biscuit.

Had it not been only the week before that they had gazed into the coffin of Peggy Kelly? Peggy had been in their class at school until taken by consumption, the illness sent from heaven. Father Sullivan said it was because the angels had requested the pleasure of her company.

The small parlour had been filled with people, and every few minutes a little woman, who was an aunt of Peggy's, sprinkled perfume over the coffin. Mrs Kelly, a very fat woman, sat in a rocking chair saying her rosary. Every so often she would rock backwards and forwards, howling with grief that the angels had been so inclined to take her little daughter. Then, in one of her rocks, she had broken wind quite loudly, causing the two boys to giggle. They looked at each other and tried not to giggle, then they tried not looking at each other but they still giggled. Finally they spluttered bits of arrowroot biscuit into each others' faces, and the little aunt had snatched the cups of ginger beer from them and pushed them out into the street.

The Devil had still not shown himself, and both lads had half a mind to go chasing cats after all. And then from the window appeared a black bowler hat. The boys were afraid. They wanted to run, but they couldn't. After a couple of seconds Kevin pointed out that it couldn't be the Devil, because his father had always told him that a black bowler hat was the mark of decency and respectability, so it was hardly likely the Devil would put a black bowler hat on to the side of his head like his father did before he went to the pub on a Saturday night. Kevin was sure the Devil looked more like the joker in a pack of playing cards.

Indeed, it wasn't the Devil after all. It was Mr O'Rourke the undertaker, who had come to remove the body. Not wishing to offend the neighbours by taking the body out through the front door – her being a suicide – he had told his men to take it through the back yard and down the entryway, even though it meant having to tread carefully over a broken sewer grid and stepping sideways to avoid kicking the dustbins.

The two boys raced round the corner and up Hilkirk Street, then under the archway into the cobbled courtyard of Aloysius O'Rourke and Sons, Undertakers and Furniture Removers – only to find that another tradition had been broken. Whenever there was a funeral, Kevin and Patrick were paid one penny each by Mr O'Rourke for rubbing boot-blacking on the horse's hoofs. This was so that every bit of the horse pulling the hearse would be as black as the ace of spades.

'We'll not be bothering this time,' said Mr O'Rourke. 'There'll be no fancy funeral. She'll be buried with the paupers in the Queen's Park plot – her being a suicide and that. And there'll be no black plume on the horse either.'

Kevin asked Mr Aloysius why Kathleen Murphy had killed herself, with him being an expert in the ways of the dead.

'She had too many uncles,' said Mr O'Rourke. 'She had uncles she'd never seen before or would ever be likely to see again, and she would bring an uncle home on Saturday night and he would stay till the bells was ringing for Mass on Sunday morning. So all her neighbours got up a petition and sent it to the Town Hall, saying the likes of her was not fit to live among decent folk, and she should be turned out of the house. And it was after the Town Hall wrote to Miss Murphy that she put her pennies in the meter and turned on the gas. Ah, but 'tis not something to be bothering your head with, you not being a young girl.'

Next day it seemed to be all over and done with. Most of Kathleen Murphy's near neighbours used the back entry so as not to be seen in public; and neighbours who were compelled to brownstone or donkeystone their steps for the sake of decency tried not to look at each other.

Kevin ran home as he always did, and waited for his father to come in from work. His father was a Dolly Varden man; a middenman, or a muckman. He'd once told Kevin that the name 'Dolly Varden' came from the hats they wore. When muckmen tipped iron middentins over their shoulders into the cart, ashes and tea-leaves and all sorts of things fell over them, so the men wore wide-brimmed ladies' hats like a music-hall singer, Dolly Varden, used to wear. The horse that pulled the cart was named Roscoe, and sometimes they put a lady's hat on Roscoe.

His father went to work at four o'clock in the morning, and he carried a basket with a lid which held three brews of tea in condensed milk, and half a loaf of bread with cheese, all screwed up in newspaper. Ah, but it was the bringing home of the basket at five o'clock in the evening which mattered most to Kevin, because more often than not the basket contained broken toys, torn comics and books with pages missing which his father had rooted from the bins.

'We emptied the suicide's bin today,' said his father.

'And was there much in it?' asked his mother.

'Devil a bit! Hadn't the second-hand man and the ragbone man helped themselves to anything worth taking? There was a bundle of letters tied up, and as none of us could read we chucked it in the furnace; and there was a couple of books we gave to the time-keeper, him being able to read, though he said 'twas double dutch, them being French and shorthand, whatever in tarnation shorthand is.'

'French and shorthand! My word, but didn't her ladyship fancy herself, then, and no mistake!'

'And there was this old thing.' He brought a teddy bear out of the basket and put it on the table. 'I thought 'twould do for the baby next door.'

Oh, how Kevin wanted that teddy bear. There was an ear missing, but its two bright glass eyes begged him to hug it; asking to be given a warm home and to be made restful and comfortable for ever and ever. But how could a boy ask for a teddy bear? They'd laugh at him, they would; they'd all laugh at him.

'May the Lord forgive you for bringing this evil thing into the house!' shouted his mother. 'It could have been in the very room where she took her menfolk, and where she . . . well, where she . . . and I do believe it still has the smell of gas about it. I don't want to look at it!'

She flung the teddy bear on the fire. For a second it was still a teddy bear, and Kevin's hands wanted to pull it from the fire and cuddle it and lie it down on a white pillow. But they'd laugh at him; oh, they would. So he let it burn away. The eyes still begged him for mercy as they fell down among the glowing coals.

He asked for the candle to be lit, and he went straight to bed. She shouldn't have burned the teddy bear. He blew the candle out quickly, for the flame might have come from the same flame as the teddy bear. The room was black as ink. He was afraid of looking towards the window.

Kevin was nine years old, and a very bright nine at that; but for the life of him he could never understand why he was supposed to be Irish, and his parents were supposed to be Irish, and everybody in the whole blooming district was supposed to be Irish, and yet they were living in Manchester, which was supposed to be in England, and them all singing drunken songs on a Saturday night about the Irish killing the English.

He knew a lot of people who were not English, but were also not supposed to be Irish; they were supposed to be Italians, and they lived a dozen streets away. There was one particular Italian girl in his class that he wanted to know better. Her name was Vera. She was about the same age as himself; her hair was shiny black, and her complexion smooth and brown; she was not a bit like the white-faced, freckled, red-haired Irish girls whom he normally threw half-bricks at.

Her father played 'Sweet Rosie O'Grady' on a barrel-organ in the streets, and he used to stop turning the handle occasionally to wipe his running nose on the sleeve of his old overcoat, which was far too big for him anyway and came down to his boots. Kevin wanted to marry Vera, and the gang said it would be okay because she was a Catholic, even though she was not Irish.

There was, sad to say, one snag to this desired romance, and that came in the size and shape of his pal Patrick Devlin. If ever there was a nine-year-old whose surname contained all the letters of Old Nick himself, it was Patrick; and wasn't it Patrick who was always boasting he'd seen the Devil, and the Devil had raised his hat to him and winked? Didn't the girls in the class just stare at him with wonderment? Vera's eyes were only for Patrick.

And Patrick's father was notorious, and known throughout Ancoats as 'the Yank', because he'd once set off from Tralee to make his fame and fortune in America, but he'd spent all his passage money on strong ale and porter in the quayside pubs of Cork, and had been left with only enough cash in his pocket to take him to England. All Kevin's dad had done to get to England was sell an old piano that nobody could play, and was broken in any case.

But it was at confession on Saturday evening when Patrick really came into his own.

The boys sat in the pews at the back of the church on the left side of the altar; and the girls sat on the right. When the tiny bell tinkled for the beginning of confession, Patrick always got up first and strode like a hero up the aisle. He wore the heaviest of wooden clogs, studded all round with steel rivets, and they sparked upwards and everywhere from the stone floor, offering positive proof that he had some sort of connivance going on with the Devil.

Many of the girls, including Vera, made the sign of the cross. The boys were a little embarrassed and pretended to look at the statue of Saint Anne.

When Patrick left the confession box after the usual minute inside, he would creep without so much as a spark to the front pew in front of the altar, far away from the other youngsters, as though he had been ordered to keep his distance from them. And then his contrition would begin. He would mumble away ninteen words to the dozen, glancing repeatedly at the suspended crucifix, and beating his breast as though in pain of purgatory.

He must be a sinful boy, the girls all thought. He must have been given hundreds of Our Fathers. What wicked sins had he committed?

One by one the children went in to the priest. They came out and gabbled their penances, and within minutes the boys were outside the church calling each other names, which usually ended up in a fight. But most of the girls stayed behind to watch Patrick beating his fists against his forehead and sometimes stretching out his arms in supplication to Christ on the cross. Let us pray for his soul, the girls would whisper to each other, and Vera was always the first to start on her rosary beads, the ones her grandmother had sent from Rome.

Eventually Patrick would stand up like a martyr about to save Ireland, and he would click-clack and spark out of the church. The devoted girls would follow him down the street at a safe distance; the more daring ones would chalk his name and their initials up on a wall, then run away in case he looked around.

To Kevin it became as plain as the nose on his face that if he wanted the Italian girl to look at him twice he would have to beat Patrick at his own game; he'd have to demonstrate he was the better sinner of the two.

This would not be easy. He had no experience of previous sinning, and at his age there were not all that many sins open to him. For a long time after taking his first Holy Communion he had gone nervously into the confession box to tell the priest that he had nothing to confess, for which he had been told to say three Hail Marys, presumably as penance for wasting the priest's time. Then he had bought a sin from Terence Mahoney for a penny. It was a very ordinary sin, and only worth a penny – simply that he had argued with his mother and father. When he told it to the priest, he still got three Hail Marys; it was disappointing but better than confessing nothing.

Kevin was fully aware that three Hail Marys would get him nowhere against Patrick Devlin's half-hour of breast beating. It would be the equivalent of a knock-out in the first ten seconds of the first round. He would have to study tactics.

But a Saturday evening arrived when Kevin realized it would have to be then or never. He had seen chalked up on a cotton mill wall that Vera loved Patrick.

The Devil's boy, little guessing he was going to be challenged to a duel, click-clacked and sparked his confident way into the box. No sooner had he staggered out than Kevin went in.

'Bless me, father, for I have sinned. It is two weeks since my last

15

confession. I hate my father because he sold a piano to come to England when he could have tried to get to America, which is where Laurel and Hardy live, even though he might not have been able to afford the fare because of spending the money on beer.'

'Go in peace, and God bless you, my son,' said the priest. 'Make a good act of contrition and say three Hail Marys.'

Kevin crawled out of the box, defeated. Even the priest was on Patrick's side. And then the truth wafted across to Kevin as strong as the smell of frying onions. It was all an act on Patrick's part; he was putting it on. A boy could kill everybody in the whole world and get no more than three Hail Marys from Father Sullivan. Well, then *he* could cheat too!

Patrick had already banged his breast several times before Kevin knelt at the front pew on the opposite side of the altar and tore his hair. Patrick slapped the palm of his hand on his forehead; Kevin pulled his fingers until his knuckles cracked. Patrick stretched his arms out to Jesus on the Cross; Kevin appealed to the tranquil Madonna.

Some of the boys who were already leaving the church to have a fist-fight in the street returned to their pews. They sensed that a duel of the damned was taking place, and soon the heads of boys and girls were turning left and right like spectators at a tennis tournament. Patrick had a theological advantage. He, a suffering sinner, was appealing directly to a suffering Saviour. Kevin on the other hand, begging forgiveness from the statue of the Blessed Virgin, felt like a bit of a sissy, as though he were telling tales to his mother. He changed his strategy and wandered around the church asking forgiveness from all the statues of the saints. Patrick stopped suffering and turned around to watch.

There was Saint Francis of Assisi patting an animal, and Kevin kissed the toe of the saint. The statue had not been cleaned for a long time; dust got up his nose; he sneezed, but he was able to turn the sneeze into a yell of anguish. When he turned to the open-mouthed children, his nose was jet-black with dirt. To non-Catholics he might just have been trying to look like Mickey Mouse; to the Catholic children who saw him, this was a stigma like Sister Bridget had been telling them about.

Patrick could not follow that. He conceded victory by leaving the church without even attempting to raise one small spark from his clogs.

Kevin prayed on for a few minutes, then he too staggered out of the church, followed by the girls. Vera came up to him.

'I was praying for your soul all the time,' she said.

'I know where there's a dead cat,' he replied.

'Will you take me to see it?' she asked.

He escorted her down an entry between two mills to the hump-backed cobbled canal bridge, and he pointed to a dead cat which had been lying in a gutter for several days. The sight made them both feel sick.

'When we grow up, will you marry me?' he asked.

'I don't think so,' she said.

'I'll be a Dolly Varden man by day, and a street fighter by night, and sure I'll make a lot of money, and we'll be able to live in Raglan Street, half-way between your parents and my parents. And I'll take you to the Palmy Picturedrome every night when you're not having babies, and half the babies can be Italian, and the other half can be Irish.' He felt his face becoming hot as he talked, but he knew that what he'd said had to be said.

'Hey, wait!' she said. 'I could never marry such a sinful boy as you; I'd be saying the rosary for you all the time. That was a big long penance. What sins did you commit?'

The gang was all together under the railway bridge. It was a good place to be because it was raining like it had never rained before. There were Liam, Patrick, Michael, Terence and Kevin. It was a sort of pilgrimage, for the railway bridge was none other than the Fenian Arch. Liam knew the story by heart, and was never tired of telling the others.

'There was two bold Fenian men being taken to Belle Vue jail in the paddywagon pulled by mighty horses and guarded by fearless Saxons. Then down from the banks of the railway – just where that cat is now shitting and scratching the dirt over its shit – came running and jumping a hundred brave Fenians, and there was the hell of a schemozzle, and then they heard the thunderous roar of policemen galloping towards them. Well now, the bloom- ing old police sergeant looked out through the keyhole to see what the shenanikin was all about, and by a bit of an accident somebody let rip a shot from a gun to blow out the keyhole, and the sergeant's brains was splattered all over the place. Then they dangled three Irish martyrs by their necks from twirling ropes for all Manchester to see, 'cos they said it was murder; but it wasn't murder, for wasn't it the blooming sergeant's fault for peeping through keyholes?'

'I'd like to die for Ireland when I grow up,' said Kevin.

'I'd like to be hanged from a scaffold high,' said Patrick.

'I'd like to be shot before a firing squad,' said Liam.

'I'd like to be drowned,' said Terence.

'You can't,' said Liam.

'And why not?'

'Because when you opened your mouth to say God Save Ireland you'd get a gob full of water, and the words would come out bubbles, and nobody would know what you were being drowned for.'

The story of the Fenian Arch fascinated the boys, but it gave rise to some unanswerable questions. Belle Vue wasn't a jail, it was a zoo, with a massive monkey-house full of hundreds of monkeys. There was in fact a song which the boys sang after old people or anybody else who was unable to chase them:

> *All the monkeys in Belle Vue*
> *Have their backsides painted blue,*
> *Just like you, just like you.*

So why were the two Fenians being taken in a paddywagon to the monkey-house?

'Maybe to have their backsides painted blue for stealing?' suggested Terence, and it was generally agreed that the English were very strange people.

The other question was – what were Fenians? All they could get from their fathers was that it was not a subject to be talking about, but it was the Fenians helped make Ireland free.

The gang decided to play at being Fenians, and climb up the railway embankment and hide and throw stones at people who passed under the bridge, and the fact that they might get hanged for it added great excitement to the proposed adventure. Their first ambush was a reasonable success. Michael had managed to acquire a water pistol, and he promised the rest of the boys he would obtain water pistols for all of them as time went by.

They lay low among the weeds of the embankment, and when

anybody passed by on the pavement below they squirted water on them. The victims assumed it was rusty water dripping from the bridge, and they merely put their coat collars up as they went on their way.

The Fenians however suffered a casualty. Liam knelt down in a big heap of cat muck and he began to stink terribly. He stank so badly that his comrades made him walk several paces behind them when they were going home.

Liam's mother gave him a solid clout, and another clout, and another clout, and called him a filthy little tinker and demanded to know what he'd been doing to get muck all over him? He said he'd been helping to set Ireland free, and got another clout, and another clout, and was made get into the tin bath for a good scrubbing with carbolic soap. And then he was sent early to bed without a candle. He put his head under the blankets and whispered to himself, 'What matter if for Erin's cause we fall.' It was something his dad always sang when he had drink taken.

The ambushes became better and better, especially since Michael began supplying them with water pistols in exchange for cigarette cards and glass marbles, and none of the people who got wet ever twigged. They always blamed the bridge.

Then there was one night they decided to crawl along the embankment to the next bridge, just for the hell of it. And didn't they just stumble on some more kids down in the weeds at the next bridge, playing the same game?

'And who the blazes are you?' asked the big boy of the new bunch.

'We're us,' replied Kevin. 'And who the Devil are you?'

'We're us too. And we were here first.'

'Is that so?'

'Aye – that's so, so it is.'

The dialogue could have become dangerous and repetitive had Liam not recognized the boys as being from Saint Malachi's.

Because of his father's habits, Liam was on marble-playing terms with most of the immigrant children of the city. He and his dad normally went to Saint Anne's except for when it was time for his father to go to confession and make a good act of contrition, at which times his dad took him to a different church like Saint Malachi's, Saint Alban's and Saint Aloysius's, because he said it didn't do to let Father Sullivan know all that was going on.

'We're playing at Fenians,' said one of the Malachi boys.

'So are we,' said Liam.

'You can't be, for the Fenian Arch is ours.'

'Oh no, it isn't. We've got the Fenian Arch – it's ours. That's where we've just come from.'

'Our dads have all taken us to the Fenian Arch, and this is it. Over Ashton Old Road!'

'The Fenian Arch is over Hyde Road, and my dad knows more than your dad.'

'Ashton Old Road.'

'Hyde Road.'

'Prove it.'

Without saying much more to each other, it was fairly obvious that the only way to find a peaceful solution as to which was the correct Fenian Arch was to fight for it. Neither the Saint Anne's boys nor the Saint Malachi's boys were prepared at the moment.

'We'll be back on Friday night,' said Kevin for Saint Anne's.

'And so shall we,' said Brian for Saint Malachi's.

It was decided that water pistols might be fine for squirting over unsuspecting under-bridge walkers but were no use for mortal combat. When Irish kids were about to fight Irish kids, something more effective in the way of armament would be needed. So they wrapped bits of brick up in newspaper, tied them round and round with string, then tied a long piece of thicker string round the bundle in order to swing it.

Friday night was very foggy, and the boys were only able to find their way to the Fenian Arch by going from one yellow circle of lamplight to another. Because of the fog the trams had stopped, and it was quiet everywhere. They reached the bridge and clambered up on the embankment, and Liam put his knee in some cat muck again but he knew his mother wouldn't notice the cat muck when she was crying over his dead body. The boys crawled and slipped and slithered along the embankment towards the other bridge. It still remained silent, and they gradually felt brave enough to sing:

> God save Ireland said the heroes,
> God save Ireland sing we all . . .

They stopped singing. And then they heard the selfsame song

coming towards them through the fog. Soon the two gangs met up, and from a light high above the railway lines the Saint Anne's boys were able to see that the Saint Malachi's boys carried sticks with dustbin lids as shields.

The fight began. There was whirling, whizzing and hitting and thumping and kicking and shouting. They fell over each other and rolled over each other. Faces started to bleed, and knuckles started to bleed, and knees started to bleed. Dustbin lids rolled down the embankment. Sticks were snapped, and many was the thud of brick on head.

And then suddenly there was the most unholy explosion. The boys flung themselves flat. There was another ear-blasting bang.

'What in the name of God was that?' whispered Brian.

'We're being shelled,' said Liam. 'It's Britannia's Nuns with their long-range guns. Me father told me about them.'

There was another explosion – this time closer.

'To hell with this,' said Brian. 'We're going home.'

'And us,' shouted Michael. The boys scrambled down the slope and on to the road. It was all right for the Saint Malachi boys – they were in their home territory. But the Saint Anne's lads were lost, and they had no intention of scuttling back along the embankment to their own bridge. Another explosion came, nearer still. They were frightened and wanted to run, but the fog surrounded them like a brownish-grey wall, and seemed to hold them like in a clenched fist.

'Never wanted to be a hero.'

'Neither did I.'

'It was your idea.'

'No, it wasn't – it was yours.'

Suddenly a figure came at them through the fog. It was Police Constable Donovan.

'What're you lot doing?'

'Nothing, sir.'

'Nothing? You've made a right bloody mess of yourselves doing nothing. You've been fighting, haven't you?'

'We've been playing war.'

'Oh aye – and who won?'

'Us. We were the English and they were the Germans.'

'You'll wish you'd been neutral when you get home. I wouldn't like to be in your shoes when your mothers see you.'

Once more there was an explosion, and the boys grabbed at Constable Donovan.

'Don't let them get us!' shouted Liam.

'Them's fog signals,' said Constable Donovan. 'Fog signals to let the trains know when they go over them. Come on, I'll see you home.'

'I knew they were fog signals,' said Kevin.

Fifteen minutes later, Liam stood outside the door of his home. He made a quick sign of the cross and said, 'Dear Jesus, I'll bet your mother, the holy blessed Virgin, wouldn't have clouted you if you'd been playing Fenians and come home with cat muck and blood on you. So please don't let it happen to me.'

His prayer apparently didn't get through because of the fog. A few minutes later he was being clouted and scrubbed, and his mother was asking all the saints what sins she'd committed to be cursed with such a boy. He went up the stairs without a candle.

But after a time his father came up with a candle and sat down on his bed, and wanted to know what it was all about. Liam told him as best he could.

'Hyde Road is the real Fenian Arch, isn't it, Dad?' he asked.

'Would I tell you it was, if it wasn't?'

'But what about the bridge over Ashton Old Road?'

His father twirled his moustache and thought. Liam knew his father was a clever man and could have been a famous doctor and cured the whooping cough if only he'd been able to read and write.

'Suppose,' said his father, after thinking, 'now just suppose that there were two paddywagons with two prisoners in each and a police sergeant guarding them in each paddywagon –'

'I like police sergeants,' interrupted Liam.

'That's a different matter,' said his father. 'Now suppose each paddywagon was going up a different road at the same time, and the Fenians caught on to it, and they made two separate ambushes, and shot two separate sergeants, and they hanged two from one and two from the other? What about that, now!'

'D'y'think that's what happened, dad?'

'With the English, my boy, anything can happen. Sure they're a scheming, conniving bunch of people, and I wouldn't put it past them.'

22

In bed that night Kevin wished he'd been one of the martyrs hanged for Ireland, for he realized Vera would never be his now, and that his only hope was to show her he wasn't such a black and sinful boy after all. An opportunity was sneaking up on him sooner than he thought.

The next day, after morning Mass, the clinic woman came to inspect heads for lice. Each child had to step out to the front of the class and be examined. Father Sullivan stood by with the strap in his hand in case anybody became rebellious. Kevin was the only boy to have no lice in his hair; and Father Sullivan frowned, not liking any child to be better than another. Kevin had a clean head simply because his mother, who seemed to enjoy it, went through his head with a steel louse trap every night. If there were any lice, they fell on to a newspaper spread over the table; and his father, who definitely enjoyed the exercise, would crack any lice with his thumbnail, saying 'There goes another little bugger!'

And then, after a whispered consultation with Father Sullivan, who nodded an agreement, the louse lady announced. The firm which made red coloured soap called 'Lifebuoy' was awarding 'clean hands certificates' to all schoolchildren who washed their hands every day for a month. Mr Rocca would inspect their hands twice a day; although Father Sullivan added that it mattered not if a boy or girl had lice in their hair or dirt on their hands as long as they could present a lily-white soul to Our Lord Jesus Christ.

Kevin wanted that certificate desperately. He wanted to show it to Vera, to prove to her that he was clean and not sinful.

For the first few days everybody in his class turned up with clean hands; but gradually they were eliminated one by one – all except Kevin who once again incurred Father Sullivan's frown for being different. The other boys didn't exactly resent Kevin for having clean hands; they liked him, and they wanted him to remain one of them. They were determined he would not get the certificate.

On the morning of the last day, they formed a group around the school door, and as Kevin was about to go in one of them shouted 'catch'. He instinctively cupped his hands to catch whatever it was which had been thrown. It was soft and wet dog muck.

Kevin panicked. He ran into the cloakroom, but the taps were out of order. He wiped his hands down somebody's raincoat hanging on a peg, but that only spread the muck. He couldn't tell

23

Mr Rocca what his friends had done. He was too far from home to run back. Then he suddenly remembered the Protestant school across the road; perhaps their taps were working. He raced out of the building and across the street. He met Arthur, a lad he knew slightly, going through the gate.

'Quick. Where's the cloakroom?'

'Follow me.'

Arthur led him to the cloakroom and stayed with him while he cleaned his hands. Then out of the blue came a teacher.

'What are you two doing in here? The bell's gone. You should be in class. Now, go on! Get in the classroom this minute! Hurry up!'

He pushed them into a classroom. There was an empty desk and Kevin stood by it, shivering with fear. The teacher flapped his hand downward for them to sit. They sat. Then he called the register. One or two children stared at Kevin, thinking he was a new kid – for new kids came and went. Presumably the teacher thought the same.

There were one or two things about this strange classroom which excited him. It was mixed: there were girls as well as boys in the class. And there were no pictures of the Sacret Heart or the Virgin Mary on the wall; instead, there was one of an elephant and one of a giraffe.

'Now then,' said the teacher, 'who can tell me what happened in the year 55BC?'

There was a silence. He repeated the question, reminding them that he had mentioned it only yesterday. Arthur put his hand up.

'Yes, Arthur!'

'Please sir, it rained.'

'It may have done indeed. And no doubt there was the usual amount of sunshine, but that is hardly history. Unless I get a proper answer, you'll all be kept in at play-time.'

This was a terrible shock for Kevin. Play-time should have been his escape, and they might turn him into a Protestant, and how the devil could he tell his parents and Father Sullivan that he had been made a Protestant because of the taps in the cloakroom?

'Please sir, the Romans came,' he shouted.

'Very good. And who led them?'

24

'Please sir, Julius Caesar, and he was bald, so there was no lice in his hair.'

The teacher turned his back to the class and shook as though he were laughing, but he soon faced the class again.

'You lot have this new boy to thank for saving your play-time,' he said. Some of the girls turned round and smiled at Kevin, and he knew they had fallen in love with him, and it made him fidget. But there was one girl who didn't look at him. She was looking at the giraffe, but he could see her face in the glass of the picture and knew that she was looking at him through the giraffe; and he realized that he loved her, whoever she was, better than Vera.

As soon as the lesson was finished he slipped out of the classroom and ran hell for leather back to Saint Anne's. He showed his hands to Mr Rocca, who asked him where on earth he'd been.

'Well, if ye'll believe me, sir, me mother was very ill and I had to run to the doctor in Ardwick, then come back and buy her some comics and bananas.'

But the fat was in the fire that evening when Father Sullivan called round to visit his mother, her being very ill and that; but she told the priest she'd not had a day's illness in many a long year. Father Sullivan patted Kevin on the head and said he'd be wishful to be having a few words with him after Mass in the morning.

''Tis a disastrous calamity to tell a fib,' he bawled at Kevin the next day. 'But when a boy tells a lie about the mother who gave him birth being ill, then to be sure the Devil will already be shaping a shovel for that boy to stoke the everlasting furnaces with.'

'Bless me, Father, for I have sinned.'

'Tell me the truth now. Was it fishing old bedsteads out of the cut to be selling the brass knobs to the old scrap dealer, you was up to? What was it? What was it, now! The truth, or ye'll be turned into a goat.'

Kevin told him the truth. He even confessed that the soap in the Protestant school had been white instead of the red he was supposed to use. At first he thought the priest was going to explode with anger, but then Father Sullivan turned to the window and looked out, and, like the Protestant teacher, appeared to be laughing. But he wasn't laughing when he turned back to Kevin.

'Do ye know what ye are? Ye're a heretic!'

'Yes, Father.'

'And do ye know what they did with heretics in the good old days?'

'They burned them at the stake, Father.'

'They did that. And do you deserve to be burned at the stake?'

'Oh, I do, Father. I do indeed.'

'Aye, so ye do. But I'm sorry to say 'tis against the law in this heathen land of England. But ye'll agree ye must be punished for them heretical gallivantings of yours?'

'Yes please, Father. Thank you, Father.'

The priest led him back to his own classroom, where he was made to stand at the back with his arms folded and wearing the dunce's cap, a tall conical cardboard hat with the letter 'D' on it. In accordance with tradition, for the length of time he wore it he did not exist; and Mr Rocca brought the point home by frequently asking where Kevin was.

He had gained the 'clean hands certificate' but he no longer wanted it. In earning it, some of his friends had become enemies; on the other hand, some of his enemies had become friends. He felt he loved the giraffe girl better by far than Vera; but she was a Protestant, and God had divided them; he would never see her again.

He ran into the street with his four loyal friends after school. Across the street was the mad monk, picking up cigarette ends and limping with one foot in the gutter and the other foot on the edgings. The gang began pelting the mad monk with dog muck and horse muck. Even when muck landed on his face, the mad monk neither ducked nor winced. Kevin looked at his clean hands. They didn't have to stay clean now he had won the certificate; so he scooped up rolls of horse muck and flung it at the mad monk along with the rest of the gang.

The mad monk was about forty, which to the children of Ancoats was old. He wore a torn and dirty raincoat which came down to his ankles and was tied around his waist with a skipping rope. His head was covered by a piece of sacking fastened under his chin with a pink ribbon. His boots were army boots, many sizes too big. Every day without fail he would be in the same streets at the same time picking up cigarette ends from the flags and gutters.

The girls ran away from him; they were afraid he would take them down an entry and do horrible things. The boys threw everything they could at him; sometimes, though not often, he raised his hands to hit them and made noises which were more like a wild animal than a human being.

The boys said he was a mad monk called Rice Pudding. They'd heard the name Rice Pudding being used for a mad monk. Besides, he behaved like a mad monk; he was always outside a church when the bells were ringing, whether it was a Protestant church to tell the time, or a Catholic church to ring the Angelus or chime The Lourdes Hymn. And he looked like a mad monk with his long coat tied round the middle and the canvas sacking over his head. Picking up cigarette dimps in the street was probably his way of becoming a saint, like Saint Francis had fed pigeons. Stoning him would be helping him on his way, according to the kids; for had not Father Sullivan himself said that all the best saints were stoned before they died?

The mad monk banged on the back door of his home in Beswick Street; his mother had told him never to use the front. She came slithering out in her dirty slippers, and flung her arms around him. She wiped the muck off his face with her tattered pinafore.

'Chuckie! My lovely little chuckie!' she said. 'There's no water to wash your face; the tap is frozen. But I managed to get enough icicles – lovely little icicles – to put in the kettle, and it's singing away to itself on the hob, and you'll soon have a nice warm cup of tea. And there's a pan of tripe and pigs' trotters. I'll take your bag off you. Ooooh, there's a nice lot. You're a clever little chuckie! The lavatory is frozen so try not to use it. Heaven help them next door, with seven in the house.'

She took him in, sat him by the fire and removed his raincoat and his boots and the sacking around his head. He was completely bald, and his jaw sagged when she untied the pink ribbon.

He supped his tea from an enamel mug, and a lot of the tea dripped down his chin and under his neck. He put spoonfuls of tripe in his mouth, although pieces of tripe fell down his shirt. He gnawed at the pigs' trotters, then cleaned his tin dish up with a piece of bread. Throughout the meal, his mother both praised him and scolded him.

'That's it my little lovely – gobble it all up. Clever little chuckie!

Ooh, Donald, I do wish you'd wear some of them nice clothes Ikey Mo brings, and he gives them to us for nothing. There was that nice black overcoat, and there was that trilby hat, and what did you do? You put them on the fire and filled the house with smoke, didn't you? If you don't want them, you should give them to me to give to the ragbone man for brownstones. I haven't stoned the steps for ages, and I don't want them paddies looking down their noses at us. 'Course you don't remember but we didn't always live among the paddies. We lived in Droylsden, and your dad was a weaver and always wore a top hat to let the spinners know he was a weaver. He'd be proud of you, chuckie!'

The old lady cleared the table away, then spread some newspaper over the top. The mad monk tipped a load of cigarette ends over the table and began snipping the burnt ends away with a pair of scissors. His next task was to split the cigarette papers with his thumbs and tip out the small amounts of tobacco into a mound. His mother threw the charred ends and bits of paper into the fire, then she put a large square biscuit tin on to the table.

The tin was nearly half filled with rolled cigarettes, and on top of them were packets of cigarette papers. She gave him one of the packets and like a machine, he began rolling and licking cigarettes; each one was perfect in shape and size, and one by one they were placed carefully in the biscuit tin.

The mad monk suddenly laughed at his mother and said, 'Ba poo!'

'You never get tired of it, do you, my little darling?' said his mother, and she went into her nightly ritual.

'Well, when you were very small, me and your daddy took you to Blackpool on the puffer train, and you couldn't take your eyes off the Tower, could you? Then me and you went paddling in the sea, and this is what we did.'

The old lady kicked off her slippers and lifted up her heavy grey skirt and pinafore. Her legs were blue and bulging with varicose veins, and she pretended she was paddling.

'Ooh, the water's cold, isn't it, chuckie? Ooh, we'll have some nice chips with salt and vinegar when we get out. Ooh, I've been bitten by a crab!'

She pretended a crab had bitten her toe, and she put her foot up on a chair and started rubbing it as though it hurt.

Her son laughed and laughed, but he still managed to roll the

28

cigarettes automatically between the laughs. Then he said, 'Day noo!'

'Oh dear, I'm out of puff,' said the old lady. 'But never mind! Well, me and your dad used to push you in the pram all the way along the banks of the Droylsden Canal to Daisy Nook every May day, and they roasted an ox, and everybody called your dad Mr Grimshaw – they always called him Mr Grimshaw. Then the fiddlers started fiddling and we'd start dancing while the fiddlers fiddled.'

The old lady started dancing around the floor and singing, *'The miller he stole bread, the weaver he stole yarn, and the little tailor he stole broadcloth to keep the three rogues warm.'*

Her son's head dropped from side to side in an attempt to sway to the rhythm, and he laughed and laughed, and once more said, 'Day noo!'

The old lady patted her breast and panted, but she started to dance and sing again, *'The miller was drowned in his dam, the weaver was hanged in his yarn, but the Devil ran off with the little tailor with broadcloth under his arm.'*

Tears rolled down her son's cheeks as he laughed at her capers. Suddenly she sat down and looked at him, and tears rolled down her cheeks too, but not with laughter.

'Oh my tiny chuckie, I hope you die before I die, because your dad will be waiting for you, then you can both wait for me. If I die first, then they'll lock you up in the lunatic asylum at Prestwich with thick heavy iron bars on the window.'

Her son grinned away at her while she talked, but he never stopped rolling cigarettes. She had to dry her eyes when somebody knocked on the front door. She shut the kitchen door behind her and went into the parlour to answer it, the parlour door leading straight on to the street. There were two small boys outside.

'Please, Mrs Grimshaw, can my dad have threepenn'orth of cigarettes?' said Patrick.

'And my dad wants twopenn'orth,' chipped in Michael.

She took the money from them, told them to wait, then went back into the kitchen where she wrapped some cigarettes up in two little rolls of newspaper. These she took back, gave them to the boys and said goodnight to them.

'God has been good to us, lovie,' she told her son when she sat down again. 'He's showed us how we can pay our way, and as long as we pay our way they'll leave us alone and they won't try to lock you up or put me in a home. There, see – pennies for the rentman's tin, pennies for the gasman's tin, and pennies for my pinny pocket to buy food, and tomorrow I'll boil you some nice cowheels. You like cowheels, don't you, chuckie?'

The night went on. Occasionally a train whistled or two cats were heard fighting on a backyard wall. The old lady made several cups of tea and a plate of porridge for her son. He used up all his mound of tobacco, and she put the cigarettes in the biscuit tin and folded up the newspaper. After that, she got the enamel bowl and poured out some warm water from the kettle on the hob, and sponged his hands and face.

'You're such a clever little chuckie, and I'm so proud of you, and your dad would be proud of you,' she told him repeatedly.

'Ink onk!' he said.

'That's right, darling – that's what the bells say. Ding dong bell, pussy's in the well! You start at the church when the bell goes ding-ding-ding, then you go up and down all the streets until you come to the church which goes dong ten times, which you count on the big piece of string in your pocket with the ten knots in. Then the next church which goes ding three times –'

'Ink onk,' he interrupted.

'Then to the next church which goes dong three times, and you count the three dongs on the little piece of string in your other pocket. And then you come to the last church which plays a pretty little hymn on the bells –'

'Ink onk.'

'That's right. And you come straight home and I'll have them cowheels all bubbling in the pan on the fire. Don't forget, chuckie – mammy can hear the bells too.'

She lit the candle in the enamel candlestick.

'Bedtime now,' she told him. 'Up the dancers for a good night's sleep, come on now! Mammy will be staying up because there'll be more people coming for your cigarettes before very long. Just see how many cigarette ends you can put in the bag tomorrow.'

They started to climb up the boards of the stairs, and he turned to his mother with a face shining with excitement and happiness. 'Day noo!' he said.

His mother tut-tutted, but she gave in and began singing, '*In good King Arthur's day, he was a jolly King, he turned his servants out of the door because they would not sing. The first he was a miller, the second he was a weaver, the third he was a little tailor, three thieving rogues together.'*

She stopped singing and pinned a newspaper to his bedroom window before undressing him.

'I'll tuck you up snug as a bug in a rug, and off you go to sleep – because I'll have to get you up bright and early in the morning while the stars are still shining. You don't want to miss the Angelus bell.'

It was the Saturday morning when Collins' Wakes came to Hilkirk Street croft. That night everything would be in full swing, and there'd not be a single solitary kid in the entire length and breadth of Ancoats who wouldn't be rambling around among the biting coke fumes and soothing sweet steam of the traction engines, staring with wonder at the fearful contraptions which Tom Collins and Sons had erected to thrill and enthral anybody who had a shilling or two to spare.

The burning ambition of every boy was to ride on the mighty dragons, but the cost was fivepence and sure that was beyond the means of most of them. So, one by one they got up early in the morning, and each set off on his own particular mission to make the money. Oh, but it would be a powerful and atrocious thing to ride the green dragons!

Kevin waited outside the tramp ward gate until the tramps had chopped their quota of firewood before being allowed loose. Eventually they shuffled out in their long dirty overcoats with their bundles of belongings, and one of them sniffed and snorted his way towards Kevin. He knew what was coming next, for he had done it so many times.

The man gave him his workhouse money and asked him to run to the chemist's round the corner and buy him a bottle of methylated spirits. Mr Clegg wouldn't serve tramps, but Kevin always said it was for his dad to clean things with.

The tramp insisted on holding the boy's jacket just to make certain he came back, and he promised him a valuable treasure on his return.

The treasure turned out to be a medal which the tramp said was

31

worth a lot of money if he took it to the pawnshop, and Kevin ran straight up the entryway to bang on the back door of Ikey Mo's because the pawnshop never opened on a Saturday.

Ikey Mo was always looked upon as a holy man by the children. He had a wrinkled forehead and a white bushy beard, and a skull cap such as altar boys wore, and he gave their parents money when they needed it. 'For you, I am doing a big favour,' he would tell them as he counted out the half-crowns.

He looked at the medal which Kevin held up, then held his hands apart like a priest giving benediction. 'My son, so I should need a Mons Star! Everybody has a Mons Star! My shop is full of Mons Stars! Now, sonny, if your mother has an old sewing-machine, for that I would pay good money.' So all that Kevin received for helping a down-and-out in need was a medal.

Patrick was given a penny by Mrs Hagan to drown a sack of kittens in the River Medlock. He carried the sack over his shoulder down to the brick-strewn banks of the black, stinking stream which was slowed down in its poisonous flow by old bedsteads, rat-gnawed mattresses, bent bicycle wheels, empty paint tins, rotted tin baths and long-since-dead dogs. He opened the sack and let the kittens tumble out.

'There you go, little cats – I'll be giving you a chance,' he told them. 'You can jump in the cut and get drowned, or you can climb back up to the street and maybe somebody'll take pity on yerz.' Patrick ran away and didn't look back. He'd earned a penny.

Michael and Terence said they'd fetch a bag of coke from Bradford Road Gasworks for old Mrs Cochran, it being freezing cold and her saying she hadn't known the warmth of a fire for two days, and that. They had a wooden box on pram wheels which was called a guider.

Mrs Cochran thanked the boys when they lugged the bag of coke into her backyard, but she said their reward would have to be in heaven because she'd only a sixpenny piece between herself and the workhouse. Michael told her to stick the reward in heaven right up her bum; in future they'd want paying in advance right here on earth; and he was about to chalk a dirty word on the front of her house until Terence warned him that God might be watching even though it wasn't Sunday.

Liam and Sean, a new kid who had moved into Dunn Street

straight from Erin, tried their luck with dead rats because they'd heard that the Manchester Town Hall paid sixpence a rat; but the Town Hall told them to piss off or they'd fetch the police, so they had to leave their bag of dead rats at the foot of Prince Albert's statue.

Anybody who didn't go to the wakes that night was a heathen or a Hottentot; a thousand boots and clogs turned the white frost of Hilkirk Street croft into slippery black mud. The air churned with smells of oil and steam, cough candy and kerosene, liquorice and treacle. A loud blab of music played 'High Over The Waves' and tried to overpower another blab which played 'The Wearing Of The Green'. Hoarse voices shouted for people to try their luck, have a go, take a chance, and come inside and see the eighth wonder of the civilized world.

The gang had no money, and it was important to ride the green dragons because only that way could a boy become a man. They stared at them. There were eight dragons chained together. They zipped like lightning and rattled like thunder on small iron wheels along up-hill down-dale tracks. The dragons were shiny green with tinted red scales. Their hell-fire red mouths were wide open. They had white hungry teeth. Their eyes were also red, and frightening like nightmares. They were terrible. They were wonderful. In the centre was a golden Saint George dressed like a Roman.

Patrick and Sean wriggled underneath the wooden steps and crawled on their bellies until the trackway was directly above them. The dragons started to roll and rumble and it sounded as though a hundred sticks were being rattled over corrugated iron. They dared not lift their heads one inch otherwise the fast-turning spiderweb of steel rods which moved the dragons would have cut their heads off for sure. They searched for any coins which might have dropped from pockets.

The other boys watched wide-eyed, expecting any minute to see a blood-dripping arm, leg or head come flying up from underneath and straight into the dragon's mouth.

Kevin felt a tap on his shoulder. His heart spun round his lungs, for it was the girl from the Protestant school. She handed him a goldfish in a bowl which had been won by her dad for shooting clay pipes because he had been a soldier and had once killed Germans. Then she ran off into the steam of the traction

33

engines, leaving him standing there with a goldfish, and the goldfish looking straight at him, and that.

Patrick and Sean slithered out from under the steps with a handful of pennies; not enough for them all to go on the dragons. But Michael had an idea inspired by the goldfish. Falling in with him, the rest of the gang dashed among the crowds asking them to come and see the human sea-lion who swallowed live fish.

A group of about twenty men, mostly black-faced men just up from the pit, gathered around Michael and told him to bloody get on with it, but Patrick went round with the bowl to make a collection first. Ha'pennies and pennies were plopped into the water and swayed to and fro to the bottom. Then Michael put his fist in the bowl, caught the goldfish, and held it by the tail above his head, where it wriggled and wriggled. He opened his mouth and swallowed it; afterwards rubbing his belly as though it had been good and tasty. Kevin stepped forward, took the Mons Star from his pocket, and pinned it on Michael's jacket.

The audience drifted away. Sean emptied the water from the bowl and started counting the coins. The other boys just stared at Michael and asked if it hurt and was he going to die?

'Ah, sure,' said Michael. ''Tis alive and happy and swimming around in my belly. You can hear it.'

He lifted up his shirt and each boy took a turn to put his ear against Michael's belly, and didn't they hear the little fish diving and turning and flicking its tail?

There was threepence more than was needed to get all the boys on a dragon, and Michael said he'd keep it to buy ants' eggs to mix with his porridge to feed the fish, and everybody thought it would be a terrible thing to do because the fish would grow and grow until his belly burst like when a lady has a baby. But there was time enough to ponder such mystical matters after the Wakes had closed with the man climbing the tower, setting himself on fire and diving headlong into a tank of water upon which oil had also been set on fire. Now was the time for the dragons.

'Hey up!' shouted Kevin as they clambered on to the seats. 'Michael, this one. Liam, this. Patrick, that one!'

The dragons rolled slowly at first, the wheels rumbled gently, the drumsticks didn't touch the drums, the cymbals didn't come together. Then the dragons went faster and faster, and their green heads wobbled and shook as they dipped down and bobbed up. The music played 'Bye-Bye, Blackbird', and the drummers drummed tattoos, and the cymbal clashers clashed and clashed. '*Pack up all my cares and woe, here I go*', the music got louder, '*Bye-Bye, blackbird*', the faces of the people watching became a whirling mass of white dots, the moon raced around the sky, '*Make my bed and light the light, I'll be home late tonight. Blackbird, bye-bye!*'

At first the boys were frightened. But their backsides and stomachs got used to the rising and falling, climbing and dipping, and they took their hands off the handrails and folded their arms to let the whole of Ancoats know they were able to ride the dragons.

They staggered off, laughing and nearly crying with excitement and achievement. They left the bright fairground to slouch homewards through the blackness of Palmerston Street. Ancoats was best at night. In the daytime the giant black mills towered over the crowded streets and everywhere was grey in the shadows; but the blackness of the night made the black mills disappear; the gas lamps were lit, and the sky flashed with tramcar flashes.

A sweet stink came up from the Medlock. It was said that the sweetness was all the fevers rising from the river; and it was also said that Aloysius O'Rourke, the undertaker, put on his top hat and black ribbons and leaned over Pin Mill Brow bridge and smiled at the river whenever it stank sweet.

Liam lifted a leg and broke wind with a loud noise. 'Catch that!' he yelled, with sheer ecstasy. Michael ripped Patrick's trouser-buttons open, and Patrick opened them still further and showed himself to a woman who was passing. 'I'm dickie-dickie-dout, and me shirt's hanging out!' he shouted at her. The gang tommy-gunned each other the rest of the way home; falling dead, rolling over, picking themselves up, then tommy-gunning again from behind lamp-posts.

Kevin blew out the candle and thought of himself as Saint George, with the little Protestant girl up on top of the gasworks bawling for help and eight evil dragons roaring and coming at him. He thought that if he thought things like that before going to sleep it would all be continued in a dream. But it wasn't. Instead, he dreamed Aloysius O'Rourke had put him in a coffin because he was dead, and all the gang was spluttering arrowroot biscuit over his face.

The gang looked down on the dead horse steaming on the frosted cobbles of Every Street. It had been whipped to get up the hill; its iron shoes had slipped on the cobbles; it had been whipped more, for the load was heavy; then it had collapsed dead, and snapped the shafts, and the bales of cotton were strewn across the street. Some men were already hacking the bales open with their knives. The carter, who had been weeping tears on the library steps, ran to his dead horse and flung his arms around its neck.

'I didn't mean to whip ye like that, me darling. But if ye'd not kept going forward, the cart would have pulled ye backward. Oh me darling, damn and set fire to the London and North Eastern Railway for putting such a load on your cart.'

The gang walked away, for it was embarrassing to watch a man cry.

'That's what this bloody Ancoats is,' said Terence. 'A bloody dead horse.'

'Sure it's worse than that,' said Michael, 'for that horse had work and was fed. Our dads have got no work, and we eat when we're lucky.'

'Aye, except him,' said Liam, thumping Kevin. 'His dad's a middenman, and they have oilcloth in their lavatory, and he doesn't wear clogs, he wears boots. Posh buggers, they think they are.'

Kevin slammed his fist in Liam's face. 'Say that again, and I'll be kicking me boots up your bum!' he yelled.

Violence might have broken out very easily, but Terence put his arm around Kevin. 'And I'll be standing up for Kevin,' he said. Then, in a confidential way, he asked Kevin: 'Your dad brings home books from the bins, doesn't he?'

'Aye, he does.'

'Could I have some of 'em?'

'No. We don't read them, we put them on the fire like peat to help out with the coal. That's why he brings them. Anyway, reading's for sissies.'

'Why do ye want books?' asked Michael.

'I can't tell you.'

And wasn't that the worst thing he could have answered, for the rest set upon him and twisted his arms and legs until he told them.

'Sure, it's me dad. He wants me to teach him to read and write, and I have to do reading and writing with him when I come home from school.'

'Why?'

'Because he says he doesn't trust tipsters, and 'tis a powerful civilizing thing to be able to choose your own winners from the list of horses in the paper, and to be able to write out your own betting slips, says he.'

There was a silence for a few seconds; then a sort of truth could be seen coming into Patrick's eyes.

'Listen,' he said, banging each one on the shoulder to show he meant what he was going to say. 'Now there's not one of our mams and dads can read or write; so suppose it got out that Terence's dad was taking up with the words, d'y'not think we'd not all be kept in at night learning our parents to read and write? 'Tis a secret which must be kept till the end o' time.'

The gang swore on the life of Father Sullivan that they'd never give away such a desperate secret. Then they noticed that Arthur was standing in their group.

'What d'y'want, kid?'

'Can I join your gang?'

'You're a bloody Saxon, aren't you?'

'I don't know.'

'You're English, aren't you, kid?'

'Yes.'

'Well, that's being a Saxon. And you're a Protestant?'

'Yes, but I live in Tutbury Street where you live.'

'Then why don't you go back to where you come from?'

'But this is where I come from. It's England. It's you micks what ought to go back where you come from.'

'Listen,' said Kevin. 'The world over, wherever a mick hangs up his hat, that is where he comes from.'

'Saxons think they're better than us,' said Liam.

'But I don't,' pleaded Arthur. 'I've got no dad, nor never had none. There's me and me mam, and we don't have oilcloth in the lavatory, and me mam gets no poor relief nor parish, and she gets money by being a totty and taking money from men for letting them kiss her. And I promise not to tell your secret about your dad learning to read and write, God's honour.'

'Let's take his trousers off and shove 'em down a grid,' said Liam. 'And he can run home showing his bum.'

The lads moved in on Arthur, but Kevin flashed his knife.

'First one as touches him gets it cut off,' he growled. 'This kid saved my life when I'd got shit on me hands. I say he joins the gang.'

'Only if he can give us a good reason.'

'I know how you can always get money to go to the kids' matinee at the bug hut,' said Arthur. 'And it's the first talkie this Saturday.'

This stunned them. They bundled him down the nearest entry so as not to be overheard. The first talkie was something they'd put at the backs of their minds because they knew they'd never get the pennies or the jam jars together. Admission to the Palmy Picturedrome for the kids' matinee was either a penny or four jam jars; the jam-jar bringers had to sit on wooden planks at the front. For months the Palmy had been sticking notices outside saying the first talkie was coming, and everybody had been talking about the talkies. Not only could screen men and women be heard talking, but their lips could be heard smacking when they kissed; bullets could be heard banging; horses could be heard galloping; doors could be heard slamming; Indians could be heard whooping; the sea could be heard swishing. It was like actually being there.

'How?' asked Patrick.

'Philips Park Cemetery,' said Arthur, and he waited for his statement to sink in before going on. 'It's full of jam jars on graves, and some of the jars have flowers in them, and you can easy get in through gaps in the railings. So we go with sacks for jam jars at night. And if there's any fresh flowers, like on a new grave, we sell them a penny a bunch outside Ancoats Hospital, which will be a bargain for they're sixpence a bunch in the market.'

There were looks of admiration. Liam burst out laughing.

'I'll tell ye what, Arthur. If all Saxons are as clever as you – coming up with jam jars from the cemetery, which is summat we'd never thought about – 'tis no wonder ye've got a bloody big empire.'

That night, Arthur knocked on Kevin's door to thank him for letting him be in the gang. He was on his way to call for Michael to raid the cemetery.

'You didn't save my life,' said Kevin. 'I fought for you to join us so that you could tell me the name of that tart in your class.'

'Which tart? There's a lot of em.'

'The one what I love.'

'I'll find out.'

'How can you find out?'

'By asking them.'

'Ye daft bastard! How can ye ask a tart if she's the one what I love? She won't know till I've told her, and I can't tell her till I know who she is. And there's summat else. There's snot coming from your nose, so either sniff it back or wipe it off with your sleeve.' He slammed the door in Arthur's face.

The seven lads were at the head of the queue outside the Palmy on Saturday afternoon; they'd got both jam jars and pennies. It occurred to Sean to ask what the talkie was about.

'Me mam's seen it,' said Terence. 'It's about a singer whose little kid of three dies, and he sings about the kid dying. You can actually hear him singing about it. It goes "Climb upon my knee, sonny boy. You are only three, sonny boy."'

'And is that it?' asked Michael.

'The tarts all come out weeping and sniffing.'

'And is that what we raided the cemetery for? And stood in this queue for? Sure we can see dead horses and dead kids any day of the week, without handing over good jam jars.'

With silent consent, the lads sloped away from the queue and went off to spend their money on cigarettes.

Christmas approached, singing its way slowly along through the fog and frost. Saint Anne's school sang 'See Amid the Winter Snow' and across the road Every Street school sang 'We Three Kings'. On Sundays the Ragged School sang 'Christians Awake' and All Souls church sang 'O Come, All Ye Faithful'. The kids who used the University Settlement sang 'Good King Wenceslas', which, having no mention of the Infant Jesus, was a fairly safe and neutral sort of song. All carols from all places were frequently interrupted by tappings of canes on desks and a teacher's voice yelling, 'No, children, you've got it wrong. Let's start again.' Miss Daly stuck her dirty little cardboard Father Christmas in her shop window in Tutbury Street; and Kevin's father began to come home from work later and drunker each day, him having been knocking at the doors and saying, 'Compliments of the Season from the Dolly Varden men!'

Came the morning of Christmas Eve, and Terence, Michael and Kevin walked down Every Street to the Horsfall Museum on the corner of Great Ancoats Street, making chalk lines along the houses as they went. It was warm inside the museum, and they went up to the Lancashire Room; normally boys didn't go in that room. It contained wooden models of cotton-making things by men named Arkwright, Kay, Hargreaves and Crompton; things which would only interest girls, because boys would never get a job in a cotton mill; it was only young tarts fresh from school who were given work in mills, and a young tart would only keep her job as long as she didn't have babies, and that. If she didn't have babies she could stay at the looms for ever and ever until she was an old biddy. The lads liked the room because it gave them a good view of Ancoats goods yard, and they could watch the trains shunting. Behind the freight yard and all around were big chimneys reaching to the sky, and all the chimneys were puffing black smoke. They were betting glass alleys on which line the next couple of wagons would be shunted when Miss Hindshaw, who was in charge of the museum, walked in. She was delighted to see three small boys talking an interest in historical things, and asked them what they'd like to be when they left school.

'A Dolly Varden man,' said Kevin.

'A priest,' said Terence.

'I want to kill Germans,' said Michael.

'Oh, and why do you wish to kill Germans?'

'Please Miss, because me dad killed Germans, and he was sent all over France to do it, and he saw all sorts of wonderful things. And sure I don't want to spend the rest of me life among all them big chimneys out there.'

The smiling lady asked them if they would like to see some of the other rooms. Michael and Kevin preferred to stay at the window and watch the shunting, but Terence said he'd like to be after seeing the secret room which was always sat outside by Mr Peg Leg who wouldn't let children in.

The room was called the Athens Room, and Mr Peg Leg was a uniformed attendant who had a wooden leg and always sat on a chair by the door. If children tried to get into the room he would lift his wooden leg as a barrier. He touched his cap when Miss Hindshaw led Terence into the room.

The poor lad wished the floor would open up and swallow him

when he stepped into the room. The whole place was very rude. He had never seen the like before. It was filled with large plaster statues, and most of them had no clothes on at all. One man had a leaf where there should have been something else; and there was a naked lady with an arm gone. All of them had something missing, and it occurred to Terence that the reason for putting the one-legged Mr Peg Leg to guard them was so that the statues wouldn't feel out of place. Miss Hindshaw told him they'd all been gods before the birth of Jesus.

Before they left the museum, Miss Hindshaw asked the boys if they'd like to go to a Christmas party at the Roundhouse in the afternoon. There would be carol singing and Santa Claus and a present for each one of them. They said 'Yes, please, Miss' and she said they would have to take part in a little nativity play which would be good fun.

The boys had to give careful consideration to this condition, for Catholics were not supposed to get involved with the goings-on at the University Settlement where they would have to mix with Protestants. Also, the Settlement Roundhouse was run by students from the University of Manchester, and it was well known that students did nothing else but cut up dead bodies all day. Not only that, but women went to the Settlement to give talks to the women of Ancoats about not having babies; yet across the road at Saint Anne's the priest was always telling the women of Ancoats to have lots of babies. This always puzzled the lads, for they were not at all sure just how tarts had babies in the first place, but what was even more mysterious was how tarts did not have babies. And then, had not both Father Sullivan and Father Granelli told the children that it was enough to have a model crib in the church at Christmas without cavorting on a stage? But the thought of a present from Father Christmas persuaded them, within half a second, to agree.

Outside, Terence told them about the bare gods he'd seen in the Athens Room.

'From what ye've told me,' said Michael, 'I'm thinking that Jesus wears a big top hat.'

'Why?'

'Because he's a world owner, like a mill owner only bigger, and he's put all them other gods out of work.'

'Perhaps that's why they'd no clothes to wear,' added Kevin.

They wandered down Great Ancoats Street to the city, for Michael had some stealing to do from Woolworths. His mother had stolen a rabbit while the man's back was turned; his father had found some vegetables which had dropped from the back of a cart; and it was up to him to steal some little presents for his five sisters. They would have to be little presents in order to fit in his pockets, and Terence suggested a crib; it could be made in a boot box with little figures. Michael agreed. He slept downstairs under some army coats, but his sisters all slept in the same bed upstairs, and he could sneak up in the dark and set the crib up to surprise them. On the way to town, Terence was asked more about the gods.

'And there was a lady god showing her big titties,' he told them.

'Ach, I don't believe a word of that.'

''Tis the truth I'm telling ye.'

'Go on, then, prove it. Spell titty.'

Terence refused to spell the word, but it started them giggling, and they shouted 'Merry Titty' to the horses under the arches of the railway stables, and through the big gates of the tramp ward, and through the large door of the men's workhouse. They shouted 'Merry Titty' in the doorways of the beerhouses. They shouted 'Merry Titty' at the trams, and one of the tram guards shouted out, 'How's your father's bald head? Same as your mother's cork leg,' and he dinged his bell to match the words. Sure, you could tell it was Christmas Eve.

Stealing from Woolworths was easy for Michael, and it didn't seem like stealing, for neither Terence nor Kevin noticed him taking things. He hung around the counter which had masses of lead soldiers and lead farmyard animals and lead zoo animals: then he went to the electrical counter to look at the Christmas-tree lights.

Kevin found a sixpence which belonged to nobody because it had rolled out of a woman's purse, and he offered to buy the lads a drink. Well, not a drink like grown-up men know it. Men went into Yates's Wine Lodge in Oldham Street; facing it was Yates's Teetotal Tavern. Both places looked the same – no chairs, no tables, but ledges around the wall, and plenty of sawdust on the floors – so it seemed like man's type drinking, except that the teetotal tavern sold only mugs of peppered lentil soup for a penny, or three ha'pence with a chunk of coarse brown bread. Customers were mostly tramps; they drank their soup with loud slurping noises; but for the élite, those who knew better, there were spoons chained to the wall with long thin chains. It was over the soup that Michael showed what he'd pinched for the crib. There was a milkmaid sitting on a stool for the Blessed Virgin Mary; there was a tiny pink piglet for the baby Jesus; there was a kneeling-down Lewis-gunner in a kilt for Saint Joseph; and for the animals who watched on that holy night there were a lion, a tiger and rhinoceros. As Father Sullivan had told them, the statues and figures of a crib were not important or holy; it was what they represented which was sacred to mankind. Michael had also stolen a flashlamp so that he could light the crib up for his sisters.

They skipped back down Great Ancoats Street, wishing the whole world a 'Merry Titty'. A telegraph boy on his red bicycle with his pillbox hat, strapped under his chin, at a precarious angle, shouted, 'Does your mother want another?' to a parcels boy who was running with his red cart and occasionally jumping in the air so that for a second boy and cart were rolling along balanced. 'Up your bum!' the parcels boy shouted back. The telegraph boy's wheels stuck in the tram lines, and for a moment he was in a groove and speeding straight towards an oncoming tram; but he managed to collapse sideways in a sprawling heap of legs and wheels before he reached it. Ah, it was Christmas Eve in the city, sure enough!

Just before reaching Every Street, the boys met Sean's father. A little dog's head poked out from beneath the man's coat.

'D'y'see that?' said Sean's father. ' 'Tis for Sean for Christmas, and it'll be at the Spread Eagle I'll be keeping it till tonight, so don't you be after breathing one solitary word about it, d'y'hear?'

'What's it called?' asked Terence.

'Spot, Rover, Towser I'm thinking.'

'How about Tiny?' said Kevin. 'For 'tis Tiny, at that.'

'Ah now, that's a wonderful name. Sure, I'd never have thought of that.'

'What's he want to go and get a dog for?' asked Michael when the man had passed. 'Doesn't it take him all his time feeding himself and his family without another mouth to fill?'

'Perhaps they're going to eat the dog for Christmas,' said Kevin.

The Settlement was full. Most of the children were from the

Protestant church of All Souls, but the children from the Ragged School were there as well, and as usual were better dressed than everybody else; which made Kevin think they changed into rags when they went to their Sunday School just to let God think they were poor, then put their glad-rags back on again when it was time to go home or to a party.

Miss Hindshaw was there, all smiling, and students in tweed jackets, grey flannel trousers, blue, grey and green striped ties with little worms between the stripes, handed out mince pies which they said their mothers had made specially for the children of Ancoats.

'Deck The Halls' was sung, and Miss Hindshaw clapped her hands to say that Santa Claus had just left Lapland. Then they sang 'Christians Awake', and she said he was getting nearer. There were more carols and more announcements until the Protestant children started stamping their feet with impatience. Terence and Michael joined with them, and Michael whispered, 'Sure, 'tis taking him a hell of a time to get from Lapland.'

Eventually sleigh bells were heard outside the Roundhouse, and in no time Santa Claus came limping and hobbling into the hall. Kevin knew it was Mr Peg Leg and told Terence, who was annoyed to think the attendant had left his gods unguarded and all on their own in a locked-up museum.

Santa limped with a sack on his back to the middle of the hall, followed by students also carrying sacks. Then Santa put his wooden leg on some orange-peel and fell arse over tip on the floor with a thud. There was a roar of laughter from the children which nearly took the roof off. The students helped him on to a chair.

'I'll be all right when I get my breath back,' he told the children, who had been threatened with the exit door unless they shut up. He showed them his wooden leg and explained, 'I got this at Gallipoli.'

'What was Father Christmas doing at Gallipoli?' a little girl asked Michael.

'Killing Germans,' said Michael.

The students went amongst the children handing out gift-wrapped presents and telling them they all had the same. The lads opened theirs. It was an apple and two handkerchiefs. Terence said it was the apple that tempted Adam and eating it would turn him into an immediate Protestant, and he ran out of the Round-house.

The smiling lady then said it was time for all those taking part in the nativity play to go backstage, and, although feeling cheated, Michael and Kevin trundled along with the others. They wondered what part they'd be asked to play; they hoped it would be the wise men from the east, then they could do their Egyptian sand shuffle in front of the manger, like Wilson, Keppel and Betty did on the music hall. That would get the other kids clapping right enough.

And there, back of the stage with other kids – God bless us and save us – Kevin saw the little Protestant girl whom he loved and would die for if called upon to do so. He was afraid of looking at her. She was dressed up like an angel.

The boys were given long white nightdresses to put on. They were told they were boy angels, and haloes would be fastened above their heads with wire, and all they had to do was look at the baby Jesus and sing 'Ding Dong Merrily On High'.

Michael was all for scrambling out through the lavatory window, but Kevin wasn't going to lose the girl he loved, so he threatened Michael that he would tell Miss Hindshaw about him stealing from Woolworths if he didn't stay.

The curtain opened. Blue lights came from the top, and red lights came from the bottom, and a yellow light lit up a girl in a blue frock, who was the Virgin Mary; and a boy in a brown frock with cotton wool on his chin, who was Joseph; and a doll in a wooden box, who was Jesus. Two rocking horses were on either side of them. Three kids came in with paper crowns on their heads, and they were the kings from the Orient. Then the girl angels danced in from the left; and the boy angels were pushed in from the right.

'We don't know "Ding Dong Whatsit",' whispered Michael.

'Just move your lips,' Kevin whispered back.

Michael shrugged his shoulders philosophically. 'Ah well, it could have been worse I suppose; sure it could have been "God Save The King".'

And then Kevin observed, from the corner of his eye, a terrible thing. The bloomers of the girl he loved were down by her shoes; the elastic must have broken. Her face was very red, and she held her knees together tightly. Kevin wished for a dragon to come roaring in through the hall, breathing fire and frightening everybody away so that he could rescue her. His face too went very red.

The boy angel next to him gave him a nudge. 'Hey, kid, look over there. That angel's keks have dropped.'

'Shut up!' snarled Kevin.

But the boy wouldn't shut up. 'I bet if you could look up her petticoat you'd see her ding-dong merrily on high.'

Kevin swung his fist into the angel's nose, and blood spurted. The angel came back on the attack, and they rolled and scrambled on the floor. Nobody noticed the little girl pick up her bloomers and run off the stage.

'Hey!' shouted Joseph. 'Them two kids is from Saint Anne's. They're bloody rednecks. Let's get em!'

A gang of lads approached. Michael and Kevin backed slowly. 'No knives,' said Kevin. ' 'Tis Christmas.'

They flung their apples at the lads who were nearest them, and a shower of apples came back in retaliation. They ripped their nightdresses off and, flailing their arms, reached the door and escaped into the street. They were bruised by the apples, and had bits of apple all over them.

There was a certain amount of triumph in Kevin's heart when he left Michael. He had fought for the girl he loved, and there was something very tingling about the thought of the girl with bloomers round her ankles. In a good mood, he screwed the two handkerchiefs back in their gift paper, and knocked on Arthur's door.

'Here you are. 'Tis a present not to be opened till the morning. 'Tis a couple of new snot rags to wipe your snotty nose on.'

As Kevin stepped out of Arthur's house into Dunn Street, there was a man being sick down a grid. He could hear a man and a woman giggling somewhere in the blackness of the entry. The chimneys had stopped smoking for a couple of days, and a few stars could be seen in between dirty grey clouds. Over the rooftops in one corner of the sky there was a white glow against the clouds from the thousands of street lamps in the city. In the house, his mother was putting the last few rags into a pegged rug. His dad had gone to midnight Mass. This wasn't Christmas. This wasn't the Christmas he wanted.

The real Christmas was in the white glow from the city.

Paper flowers of spring

Spring came to Ancoats with a vengeance. There were brightly coloured flowers in every window – although, if the truth be told, this was not because of any rustlings in the souls of the women; it was because the tinker women always came in January with their baskets of artificial flowers, threatening to curse those who refused to buy them. It was no good hiding under the table, for the tinker women would shout their curses through the letterbox. Only one woman stood up to their intimidations: Arthur's mother. Her son had given her some real flowers. They had come from the cemetery of course, but he assured her he had saved up his pennies to buy them for her; and she was so touched that she put the real flowers in her window and didn't give a damn for the tinkers' curses. This gave the impression of her trying to be better than the other women, and in no time a brick was thrown through her window to let her know.

Terence's mother bought the paper flowers, but she didn't put them in the window; instead she put them upon the piano. And why not, for wasn't hers the only piano in the district? Not like some people she could mention, *she* had not sold a piano to come to England; she had brought the piano with her, and people could say what they liked.

Nobody in the house could play the blooming old piano. His mam couldn't, his dad couldn't, and Terence certainly couldn't. And yet they'd brought it all the way from Ireland. They'd brought nothing else, for they'd nothing else to bring except a bag of clothes. Somewhere in the back of his mind, Terence could remember the piano being hoisted off the ship on to the Liverpool landing-stage; and he and his mam had sat on top of it for security while his dad disappeared for a couple of hours, to return with a handcart which had been left outside a beerhouse and nobody had seemed to own.

It seemed days and days and days. His mam and dad had pulled the handcart up and down the roads all the way to Manchester, sleeping under it at night, all three wrapped around in a shawl. Terence sometimes had rides on the handcart, but the bouncing and rattling on the cobbles going through the towns hurt his bottom so he usually walked.

Once or twice Terence had asked why the piano had been fetched all them thousands of miles from Limerick, but the only mumbled reply he could get from his mother was that it gave the house great dignity, and made them a cut above the rest. For the first couple of years it was permanently locked. This was because they'd left the key in Limerick; but eventually his father broke it open with a chisel lying lost near somebody's tool-kit.

It was the only piece of furniture they had in their rented house to begin with, the tables and chairs being orange boxes, and the bedding a heap of old army coats; until piece by piece the neighbours sold them things cheap, like a bed and a mangle and some broken chairs. But the piano stood out as something of great beauty. His mam kept it polished like glass and in a position where it could be seen by anybody passing the window.

'Maybe,' said his dad, after watching his mother place the jug of paper flowers on the piano, 'we could have Terence take up the piano? Go for lessons and that, d'y'know.'

'Will ye listen to the man! And where the hell d'y'think we'd be getting the money from?'

'We could sell the piano.'

'Are ye daft or summat? And what'd be the good of him learning to play like a merry old Trojan, and no blooming piano to be playing on? And it'd be over my dead body we parted with that beautiful instrument of music, so it would.'

'But 'tis a wonderful profession at his fingertips, and when he left school he could play up at the Spread Eagle on Saturday nights and never go short of his booze.'

'Terence is going to be a priest, and that's final. Isn't it a great blessing for a decent family, and a family with a piano at that, to be having one of its nearest and dearest in holy orders?'

Terence wanted to become a priest, and he knew he belonged to a very special family because he often heard people passing in the street and saying, 'That's the house with the piano.' And how he dreamed of paving the way for million of souls to go to heaven. All Ancoats would get away from the mills and smoking chimneys; through him their souls would rise above the rooftops and look down on what they'd left, and be thankful to him. Girls would fall in love with him, but he'd turn away from them in order to do God's work.

He began preparing for the priesthood by washing his hands and face and even his neck twice a day, for priests were always pale and clean. But the water from the tap at the slopstone was cold, and he offered Kevin twopence for his 'clean hands certificate'. Kevin's name could always be rubbed out with breadcrumbs, and his own written in; and that would impress the bishop or whoever it was that made a man into a priest.

While he was bargaining with Kevin, the man they called the mad monk shuffled his way on the other side of the street, picking up cigarette ends. 'Bless you!' shouted Terence. The mad monk didn't seem to notice, and Terence threw a tin can at him. It hit the man on the head and he snarled and bared his teeth. 'Bless you!' shouted Terence again, and he knew it was the sort of thing Jesus would have done, for Jesus blessed anybody.

The boys took Terence seriously. Kevin, although he wouldn't part with his certificate, presented him with a small plaster statue of the Virgin Mary which his dad had found wrapped up in the *Manchester Evening News* in a dustbin. The tip of her nose was broken off and had gone black.

He told his mother a nun had given it to him, and asked if it could be placed on top of the piano. His mother said no, but it could go next to the goldfish on top of the food safe in the scullery. Terence accepted that. He felt it would be company for the lonely goldfish; that in no time his fish would come to adore the statue it saw through its bowl. In any case, it was a goldfish he'd sneaked out of the classroom in its little bowl to prevent Michael swallowing it; and it must be missing the saying of the catechism, the singing of the hymns and the chanting of the nine times table. He was sure that at night when all was black the Virgin Mary would smile at the little fish and intercede for it, whatever 'intercede' meant.

He began his Hail Marys with 'I'm sorry about your nose,' and he started to act little rituals in the backyard coalshed; one attempt to make communion wine was mixing linseed oil and vinegar in an egg-cup, and being very sick afterwards.

Another sacred ritual was inspired when Baggyarse the ragboneman rattled up the street with his donkey and cart, playing

'Come To the Cookhouse Door, Boys' on his battered brass trumpet. It was said that Baggyarse had been in the charge of the Light Brigade. Terence ran out to watch them pass, for trumpets and donkeys were biblical things.

Just as the cart turned into Tutbury Street, two tattered old books fell off the back. Terence waited till the cart was far enough away, then ran to pick them up. It wasn't as if it was stealing, because nobody in Ancoats bothered with books, except for burning. Kevin had explained that peat and paper both came from wood, and books were only blocks of peat made white and covered with words.

He genuflected as he passed the Virgin and the goldfish, and rushed into the coalshed with the intention of pretending they were sacred books to be mumbled over at the altar. Then he read the names on the books. One was about the heart of a moor, and the other about a lady of the moor; one was by Beatrice Chase, and the other by John Oxenham. A man and a woman, and they had the name 'moor' in common. Shivering with excitement, Terence decided to conduct a sacrament of marriage.

He rushed back into the house and rooted out a half-used tube of glue from his mother's workbasket, then scuffled back into his tiny cathedral. He placed both books side by side on the upturned coal-bucket; then, gabbling made-up words supposed to be Latin, he smeared the sticky stuff on the backs of both books, and put the two books together, saying 'secotine secotorum' because Secotine was the name of the glue and it sounded Latin.

'You have been joined together in holy marriage,' he ended. And the glued books were placed under the goldfish bowl to live happily ever after; him telling his mother it was to lift up the goldfish so that it could look out through the scullery window.

There was no money coming into the house, and very little food except what came from the parish, but his mother touched lucky; she began to earn half-crowns from Mr Aloysius O'Rourke for laying out the dead. She'd had some previous experience, having had to lay out her mother and father as a young girl when they'd been accidentally shot by British troops in Cork, and nobody daring to come near to help her in case the authorities thought they were sympathizers with the cause.

Terence didn't altogether mind her going off at the hours to lay out the dead; in a way it was holy and sent them to heaven clean.

But he hated her coming home smelling of scented soap because Sean had once told him that totties always smelled of scented soap.

His dad definitely didn't like it. For one thing he resented her bringing home the bacon instead of him; it making him not feel much of a man. And there was sometimes a lot of shouting and swearing in the house, particularly when she'd been to lay out a man. His dad didn't mind her attending to dead women and children, but dead men seemed to make him jealous.

'Ah, sure it's not as if a blooming dead man can do me any harm,' she would say; then turning round and smiling to herself, 'Or any good either, come to think of it.' When she said that, his dad would throw something at her.

Then one day his dad walked in with a bit of good news. There was a chance of him earning five pounds.

'Five pounds! Will ye think of that, now! 'Tis the same money as you get for forty dead men. And in any case, aren't the dead falling off a bit now the winter is over, and that!'

The job was for one hour only, the best pay a man ever received. He was to be a bookie's dummy on Tuesday afternoon.

Street betting was against the law, but a house with thick curtains in Grace Street took bets up the back entry. They had a telephone; it was the only house with a telephone in Ancoats. If any stranger asked where they could put a bet on, they were shown the sky and told to follow the telephone line.

Naturally Constable Donovan knew about them, and every Friday evening he would call along to collect his two pounds. Part of his duty for the money was to inform the house with thick curtains when there was going to be a raid, for the police had to raid them every so often in order to keep up appearances. When the raid was about to take place, the regular bookie was replaced with a dummy, who was arrested, and somebody in a motor-car paid the fine.

On the afternoon Terence's dad was going to be the dummy, he put on his best clothes as though going to church, and he tapped his bowler to the side of his head. 'For sure, ye never know where an opportunity like this might lead to,' he told his wife and son.

Half an hour later there was such a commotion in the street that everybody rushed out. Terence's dad was being pulled up the street by two policemen, and he was handcuffed. He fought and kicked and pulled them, begging them take the handcuffs off and not frogmarch him with the neighbours looking on.

The magistrate decided to make an example of him because of resisting arrest with violence. Instead of a fine, he was sentenced to six months in Strangeways Prison.

Terence was cheerful enough after his mother had stopped ranting and raving. After all, many good saints had gone to prison for their faith; and did not the hymn say 'in spite of dungeon, fire and sword'? He even got his first customer for when he became a priest.

'If I pay you a penny now, will you consider it payment for marrying me and Vera when we all grow up, and no further charge?' said Patrick.

'Is it definite?' asked Kevin.

'And why shouldn't it be?' asked Patrick. 'She's got family and friends who are in the ice-cream in summer, and roast chestnuts in winter; so that's summat we'll never go short of. Sure, there's been a bit of a setback, but it'll all blow over.'

'What setback?' asked Kevin.

'Didn't a bloody lion piss all over me. But, 'tis a minor setback.'

'You're a liar!'

'That I'm not. It was me took her to Belle Vue on Saturday to see the fireworks display of the Massacre of Cawnpore, which is where the English get massacred by the wallah-wallahs. And there was time to spare so we looked round the zoological gardens, and there was a lion, and she told me there was a ruin in Rome where lions once chewed up Christians – then this lion rolls over on its side and cocks its back leg up in the air and squirts all over me.'

'You should have peed back over the lion,' said Kevin. 'It's the only way.'

'So there was me wet through and stinking, and I had to walk home while she went on the tram. And sure that's the truth I'm telling you.'

'Which way did you go to Belle Vue? Hyde Road or Ashton Old Road?' asked Liam.

'Hyde Park. But does it matter?'

'It does indeed,' said Liam. 'For ye went under the Fenian Arch, and, as ye know, going under the Fenian Arch never did no Irishman no good.'

'I'll marry ye for a penny,' said Terence. 'But not if you're covered in lion pee; especially with lions once chewing up Christians, and that.'

But a few mornings later, Father Sullivan wished to see him.

'I've a bit of bad news for you,' began the priest. 'Ye'll not be an altar boy after all, though your name's on top of the list. But 'tis like this, y'see. The sins of the fathers are visited upon by the children, so said our blessed Saviour. And there's your father now behind the bars, and it wouldn't be fair of me now – would it, now? – if I was to make you an altar boy ahead of them boys whose fathers are not yet in prison. D'y'see?'

Terence ran home with great tears rolling into his mouth and tasting salty. Home was sanctuary. But the first thing he saw, turning into the street, was two men loading the piano on to a horse and cart.

'What could I do?' moaned his mother. 'They've stopped all public assistance, being as your father's a convict. And where's the food for the table to come from? Ah, to the blue blazes with your father for what he's done to me this day!'

Terence ran into the coalshed. It wasn't his dad's fault; his dad was a fine man. It was God's fault for letting it all happen. He would teach God a lesson which God wouldn't forget in a hurry.

At the childrens' Mass on Sunday he received the blessed sacrament on his tongue, and went back to his place holding his hands tightly together; then he bent his head down low and chewed and chewed on the wafer, like a lion on a Christian. It had the taste of an ice-cream cornet. It took him seconds to munch it between his teeth. He swallowed it with a gulp.

Next Saturday he knelt down in Father Sullivan's confession box. 'Bless me, father,' he whispered. 'It is a week since my last confession. I have bitten God!'

The first thing which caught Michael's eye was a stuffed owl. His dad had taken him to a Communist Party meeting in the Working Men's Club; it was being held in the debating room, which was sometimes used by the Baptists. His dad had told him a lot about communism, but Michael couldn't connect the stuffed owl with anything he'd been told, so he guessed the owl had something to do with the Baptists.

Everybody sang about keeping the red flag flying, to a Christmas tree song he'd been taught at school. Then a man got up on the stage and talked about free meals, free doctors and hospitals, better education, and work for all. And wasn't it the hell of a surprise when his dad grabbed his hand and took him up on the stage. Michael had only been up on a stage once before in his life, and that was as an angel and had ended in a fight. But this time he felt strong and important. His father used him as an example of a typical Ancoats kid; he spoke about how many kids were being taken by consumption; and he said his son would leave school knowing only his catechism and how to sign his own name, which of course would be useful when the next war came and his son would be able to sign on the dotted line to be a soldier to get killed for the capitalists. And then his dad said Michael would tell the comrades in the hall what it was like to be a kid in Ancoats, not compared to being a kid anywhere else.

'Just tell them what ye do. How you spend your days,' nudged his father. Michael suddenly felt excited and proud. He saw himself making a speech to millions of downtrodden people who had nothing to lose but their chains. His speech would change the world. He dared not look at the individual faces of the audience because it made him just a little shy; so he made his speech to the stuffed owl at the other end of the hall.

'I collect tram tickets,' he began. 'But not tram tickets what are put back in the ticket box, because they go back to the depot. But tram tickets what are lost and lonely, and blow up the street on Saturday night when the men are in the beerhouses and the women are mending clothes. Sometimes I see a ticket floating down the rain in the gutter, and I save it before it goes down the grid. Then I take it home and put it on the hearthstone to get warm and dry. Then I put them all in a Sharps toffee tin given to me by Miss Daly, and put them under my bed which becomes their home for ever and ever, and where they meet other tram tickets. I've got all colours; even rainbow ones from them what has to catch the workers' trams at five o'clock in the morning. That's all, but if you like I can sing a song about somebody who is out of work.'

The people in the hall clapped their hands loudly, although Michael's dad seemed to frown. Michael felt very confident. He sang:

When Dixie Dean was seventeen he tried to score a goal,
He missed his chance and shit his pants, and now he's on the dole.

There was more loud applause, and Michael was given an enamel mug full of cocoa. His dad still looked angry; but when Michael offered to stay behind and clean the place up after they'd gone, his dad managed a bit of a smile.

A few days later, Michael carried a badly wrapped newspaper parcel into Ikey Mo's shop when nobody was looking.

Ikey Mo rubbed his hands with interest, until he saw what it was.

'It's an owl,' said Michael.

'It's a dead owl.'

'It's a stuffed owl.'

'Then that makes it very dead, very dead indeed. And so who would want to buy a stuffed owl in Ancoats, you tell me?'

'It's not many people have got stuffed owls.'

'It's not many people want them.'

'I once heard a man behind me praying to Saint Francis of Cissy for one.'

Ikey Mo laughed under his beard. 'And what does it eat? Stuffed mice?'

'Do owls eat mice, Mr Ikey Mo?'

'Of course they do. Didn't nobody tell you?'

'Indeed I did know that, and isn't it common knowledge? And that's why it's very useful.'

'Useful, you say! A dead crocodile is useful – it makes fine quality shoes and handbags for the ladies. A dead fox is useful – it makes an expensive fur to go round a lady's shoulders. A dead owl is not useful.'

'It will keep your house free from mice,' said Michael. 'For if you have it on the dresser or the mantelpiece, a mouse will peep out from its hole in the skirting board, and see it staring, and say to itself, "Holy Blessed Mother of God, there's an owl," and go back into its mousehole again and never come out any more, not wishful to be eaten or devoured, at all.'

Ikey Mo was delighted. He was being bargained with, and too many people begged instead of bargaining. The boy was giving him a run for his money.

'The people in the city use mousetraps,' he told Michael.

'But the people in the city can't afford the cheese for the mousetraps,' answered the boy. 'Besides, a stuffed owl doesn't kill mice, it only frightens them away, and it isn't right to kill a mouse because God made a mouse like he made a giraffe.'

Ikey Mo's eyes were lit up like flashlamp bulbs.

'Very good, and so you tell me why God made a mouse?'

'To know him, and to love him, and to serve him.'

'Why a mouse?'

'Nobody can tell you that even if you tortured them. It's one of God's mysterious secrets, and he has to keep secrets because he can't trust anybody. And anyway, Mickey Mouse is a mouse, and owls are known for being wise, even stuffed ones.'

'I'll give you a shilling,' said Ikey Mo, and he held his hands and arms out to the gas bracket as though praying. 'Abraham, Isaac and Jacob, so what do I do with a stuffed owl? You tell me – I wish to know.'

Oh, indeed – yes, indeed – Father Sullivan knew his Irish. Well, after all, wasn't he one of them himself? Had he not seen Irishmen shot by the English for no other crime than shouting 'God Save Ireland!'? Did he not remember a little cottage by the sea being battered down by redcoats while the family stood on the roof and poured boiling porridge on the soldiers; then the man being carted off and hanged on the bridge with his eyes popping out?

When he'd become a priest, his first parish was on the west coast of Ireland where there were no women for they'd all gone off to England to become nurses. There were only bachelors left digging the peat, and their only sin was masturbation, and his only advice to them had been to pray a lot and dig the peat until their hands were blistered and sore.

'I was trained to fight sin,' he'd told his bishop. 'But here there is no sin, so send me where there is sin.' And the bishop had sent him to Ancoats.

He knew that his Irish immigrants had come across in their thousands with nothing in their pockets and hatred in their hearts. They had to survive in the Protestant land of England; but he was determined they would always remain Irish and Catholic. He lectured the children on keeping their faith and culture.

Kevin held his hand up.

'You should have gone before you came in to prayers,' snapped the priest, angry with the interruption.

'Please, father, I don't want to go down.'

'Then what d'y'want? Speak up, boy!'

'Please, what does culture mean?'

Father Sullivan smiled; at least somebody was listening.

'Ah now, and 'tis glad I am you asked me that.' He chalked the word 'culture' up on the blackboard. 'Culture – and ye can all write the word out a hundred times so it'll stick in your minds – is the words and songs of the old country.'

What a bright young feller-me-lad is Kevin, thought Father Sullivan, to be asking such a question as what the hell is culture. He ought to get to know the boy's parents maybe.

Sadly, he got to know them too well.

'Am I not hearing the sounds of Ulster in your voice?' he asked Kevin's mother as she gave him tea in the only uncracked cup.

'That's right.'

'And would ye be, if I may ask –'

Kevin's dad butted in. 'Sure I'm from Kilkee meself, in the County Clare.' But the priest stared into the eyes of the woman.

'That's right, I'm a Protestant. But we was married in a Catholic church, and our boy is being brought up in your faith, so he is, so what more do ye wish? Is there anything wrong in that?'

The priest put the cup of tea down as though it had been given him by a Borgia.

'We're a mixed marriage, is that what your blooming old teacup is telling you?' went on Kevin's mother.

'Then no doubt you're a convert?'

'Sure, I never got round to it. I believe in God, and isn't that sufficient?'

''Tis not the same thing, not the same thing at all.' The priest looked around the room and noticed there were no holy pictures. 'Dearie me,' he sighed. 'Oh, dearie me. And Kevin is such a clever boy.'

'And just exactly what is that supposed to mean, will ye tell me?'

Her husband gave her a nudge. 'Father,' he said, reminding her that the priest had a title which should be used.

'Father,' she acknowledged.

'Well now, 'tis like this,' began the priest, as he pushed the teacup away from him and swept the table cloth with his hands as though preparing to explain the complicated design of creation. 'There's only one Catholic high school in this town; sure 'tis a terrible state of affairs. And therefore only a limited number of places for clever boys. As Our Lord himself said, many are called but few are chosen.'

'So Kevin hasn't a chance, is that it?'

'Now, did I say that?' begged the priest. 'Did I say that at all?' He washed his hands with invisible soap. 'Ah well, time waits for no man. 'Tis I that must be away. God bless all in this house.'

'Will ye be off and play now,' Kevin's father told him, and the lad ran out into the street, but careful not to be behind Father Sullivan. He met up with the gang in Thames Street.

Patrick joined them, sparking his clogs with pride. He'd found a purse, and there was a half-crown inside it.

'Best take it to Constable Donovan.'

'Why? He gets enough money here and there.'

'It could be somebody's.'

'It is somebody's. It's mine.'

'Somebody's rent. Or gas money. Or for food.'

'Then it serves 'em right; they shouldn't have lost it.'

Patrick spun the half-crown in the air; then dropped the empty purse down the grid. The lads ambled towards the Spread Eagle where there was always a chance of scrounging some salted crisps or a swig of beer.

As usual Blind Andy was leaning on the wall of the beerhouse playing his fiddle, with his begging cap on the flags. His hair was thin and grey; the skin beneath was dirty. He had no teeth, and his chin nearly touched his nose, which was a big nose and had a purple wart on one side of it. He wore an old army coat; the sleeves had been hacked to make them more his size. There was a boot on one foot, a slipper tied with string on the other. When he played his fiddle, which had an empty Cherry Blossom blacking tin for a sound box, his feet moved; but when he stopped playing, usually to take a mouthful of beer, the foot with the slipper tapped on the flags as though it were beating time to a silent melody going round in his head. He wore glasses blackened with boot polish, but when it rained black streaks ran down his face, and bits of glazed eyes could be seen through the glasses where the blacking had been washed away. Sometimes dogs piddled up against his legs, and he didn't notice it until his ankles felt wet. When it rained, he never noticed it at all. He wasn't allowed inside the pub even when it snowed. 'I'm not having that dirty old blind sod in here,' said Mr Kelly. ''Twill put me customers off, so it will.' However, Mr Kelly's customers always made sure Blind Andy had a pint of beer down by his feet. His favourite tunes were 'The Rose of Tralee' and 'The Lark in the Clear Air', although he played the rebel songs by request.

The lads stood and sniggered at Blind Andy. Liam had a half-packet of sherbert in his pocket, and with everybody's nodding consent he crept up and emptied the sherbert into the fiddler's half-empty pint of Guinness. Kevin, again with grinning approval, lifted a heap of dog dirt and dropped it in the fiddler's cap. Then they watched and waited.

About the place in the song where the words would have been 'that stands in the beautiful vale of Tralee', Blind Andy picked up his pot and took a long gulping swig before returning to where the words should have been 'she was lovely and fair as the rose of the summer'.

He couldn't have noticed the taste of the fizzing sherbert, for he emptied the pot, to the lads' amazement. Then Patrick walked up to Blind Andy and dropped the half-crown in his cap. His pals were even more amazed.

'Hey, you're crying!' said Liam to him when he returned to them.

'Am I hell as like crying,' said Patrick.

'There's tears coming down yer face.'

'I'm not bloody-well crying,' shouted Patrick and he fisted Liam in the face.

'Let's get his trousers down!' somebody yelled, and there was a hell of a lot of kicking and thumping; while Blind Andy had started the tune again and was at the part which would have been 'as I strolled with my love to the pure crystal fountain'.

There were only a few cuts and bruises on their faces next day in class. They were doing the coming of the Romans, when suddenly the classroom door burst open, and everybody turned round. In the doorway was Kevin's dad, and dressed in his muckman's clothes – his corduroy trousers tied with string just below the knees and giving off puffs of brown dust when he moved, a torn grey shirt with no buttons showing his body wet and

dirty with perspiration, and on his head a wide-brimmed straw
Dolly Varden hat, with little yellow blobs on a blue band which
were supposed to be primroses or something.

'Kevin,' he shouted, 'will ye be coming with me, now!'

'Stay where you are,' shouted Mr Rocca to Kevin; then to his
dad – 'And you! Just you get out of here!'

'I've come to take my boy away from this blitherin' school,' said
Kevin's dad. 'For it's a lot of thought I've been thinking while
trudging the miles, and I'm of the condensed opinion it will be
keeping him back that ye'll be up to. Come on, me boy!'

'The boy will stay at his desk,' said the teacher.

'In that case I'll be asking you to give me a hand to lift him and
his desk over the street to the other school.'

Kevin got up and walked to his dad, and grabbed his hand.
They left the classroom, and out through the gate and across the
road to where his dad's horse and cart was standing outside the
Protestant municipal school of Every Street.

'Will ye look at me!' said his dad before they went in. 'Will ye
look at me now? And is this what ye want to be when ye leave
school? A muckman? A Dolly Varden man? 'Cos that's what ye'll
be if ye stay at their blooming old school. 'Tis down they'll keep
ye!'

He was introduced to Mr Wilson, the headmaster, an Ulsterman who didn't shout as he talked like most Ulstermen. It had all
been arranged; but both men raised their eyebrows when Kevin
told them he'd been to the school before, to wash his hands.

He was plopped into his new classroom like a jack-sharp from
the canal into a jam jar. He recognized Arthur and – oh yes,
indeed – the girl he loved; she was but two desks away. The
teacher, Mr Beaumont, was kept busy for a few minutes sorting
out some papers with Mr Wilson, and it gave Kevin time to
scribble a note to her which said, 'What is your name? Will you
marry me?' The answer was passed back: 'Betty. Yes.' And
Kevin's toes twitched inside his boots.

It was strange, and everybody stared round at him; until Arthur
was called out for the strap for picking his nose, and the classroom
assumed the normality of all classrooms. There were a few
incidents at play-time when some of the heavier lads called him a
stinking holy-roller, but after displaying his skill as a gutter fighter
and leaving a few noses to bleed in the cloakroom washbasins, he

was left alone. He even got eight out of ten for adding up and taking away a lot of pounds, shillings and pence. And this made Betty look proud.

'If ye don't bring him back,' Father Sullivan told his father that night, 'you'll be excommunicated, and you know what that means; and if ye don't I'll tell ye. It means ye'll never be able to confess your sins to Almighty God; ye'll never be able to receive the blessed sacrament; ye'll burn in the fires of hell for ever and ever.'

'And maybe I'll see you there,' said his father.

'God bless all in this house,' said the priest, and left.

Kevin's father twirled his moustache in order to think; then he put his arm round his son's shoulders.

'They'll never excommunicate neither you nor me, for I've got it all worked out. Sure we'll never go to Saint Anne's again, but there's many a Catholic church in Manchester, and you and me will go to a different one each Saturday for confession and each Sunday for Mass; and that way we'll be seeing the world, and he'll never know where we are from one Sunday to the next.'

'Who won't, dad?' asked Kevin. 'Father Sullivan or God?'

Constable Donovan had been busy since the black early hours of the morning. He'd dusted down the mantelpiece and the two orange and white pot dogs which sat on either side; he'd brushed the green tasselled mantelpiece fringe; he'd blackened the grate and oven; he'd polished the brass fender. And now he unscrewed a bottle of Guinness, poured it into a silver tankard, and brought a Woodbine out from a solid gold cigarette-case. Then he watched the clock and listened to its tick-tock.

Constable Donovan kept Ancoats quiet. On night beat he avoided the railway embankment just in case a couple of men might come sliding down with bundles under their arms. If he met any man getting off an all-night tram at some strange hour he would merely say 'Good morning'. Where possible, he avoided meeting men in the middle of the night; he looked the other way. Quite often, after some midnight avoidance, he would find a gift in his backyard lavatory. He always left the backyard door un-bolted, and, as though by magic, gifts were left there; usually gifts like the silver tankard or the gold cigarette-lighter, which no pawnbroker or jeweller would touch; although these gifts were usually full of brown pee when he found them. Perhaps he should have reported the gifts, but that would have brought in the detectives, and bringing in the tecks would have been like setting a ratter dog loose in the foundations of an empty building. And sure what the hell! These men stole in order to keep their wives and kids fed and clothed and away from the workhouse.

Donovan closed a blind eye to thieves; he knew that a few years' imprisonment could put a man's wife in the workhouse and his children in a home. When young children went into the Children's Court, they could end up with six or seven years in the reformatory, and their names would be published in the paper, bringing shame on the mother and father and brothers and sisters, who would be stared at and called funny names. Better to take his belt off to them, and have done with it.

He kept Ancoats chained to its kennel, sure enough; and he did all the dirty and nasty jobs of the district.

When a man who hadn't any pennies for the gas-meter sawed through the gas-pipe and destroyed himself and his wife and five kids, it was he who had to break into the house to reach the bodies. When a baby died in its soapbox, or a child was hit by a tram, or a horse dropped dead in the tram-lines, it was he who had to touch and pull and push and arrange things. When little girls were raped down the entries, he had to carry them home, then find the man, then beat him till he was unconscious, then take him to the city police station over his shoulder.

There was the man they called the mad monk, who sloped his way along the gutters picking up cigarette dimps. He'd caught him with his trousers wide open, and had pulled him into the station, and the mad monk had been locked up in Prestwich lunatic asylum, where he belonged. A few days later he'd had to break into the house where the mad monk's mother had killed herself by putting her head in the gas oven. It had been a rotten job.

The grown-ups were set in their ways; but the kids could be disciplined before it was too late. There was the kid called Sean. His mother had come screaming round that the boy's dog had gone mad. When he got to the house, Sean was standing on the table, terrified and shouting, 'Don't, Tiny! Don't bite me, Tiny! I love you, Tiny!' A small black-and-white dog was snarling at the boy. His father had the poker in his hand, all ready to crack the dog's skull, but Sean was shouting, 'No, dad, please!'

Donovan took charge. He prodded the mother and father. 'You two, don't stand there like piffin; bring the bath in out of the yard and fill it with water as fast as you can. Look sharp, now!'

When he picked the dog up to put it in the water, it stopped snarling and even wagged its stump of a tail. He held the dog under the water, feeling its body warm and struggling as the bubbles came up. Then the bubbles stopped, and the dog was still. He lifted the drowned animal up and dumped it on the carpet.

'Me carpet's drenched,' complained the mother; but Sean screamed hysterically, 'You've killed my dog! You've killed Tiny! You've drowned little Tiny!'

'It could have had the rabies,' Donovan told him. 'And that'd have killed everybody. And if ye don't shut up that bawling and shouting, I'll skuldrag ye down to the lock-up and put ye in a cell and see how you like that!'

Then there was Terence, the dirty little sod, spending his time in the Horsfall Museum drawing men and women with no clothes on, and swapping his dirty drawings for cigarette-cards and glass alleys. He'd told him what he'd do if he ever caught him with dirty drawings again; he'd take him to the convent in Moss Side where all the swanky little girls were, and make him undress in front of them. And why had his daft old father resisted arrest— He'd told him to go quietly and it would only be a fine, which he wouldn't have to pay in any case.

Kevin he'd got to watch, for he'd all the makings of a street fighter and was a little too handy with the knife. Michael was a little thief, and he'd had to take his belt off to him in an empty backyard when he'd found the boy with half a dozen small Easter eggs together with yellow cottonwool chickens in his pockets. Patrick was always doing the fascist salute and shouting 'Good old Mussolini!', but it was harmless. And Liam was always singing the rebel songs which, too, was harmless as long as he stayed in Ancoats. 'But sing them songs where the English are, and you'll end up with a cracked skull in the gutter, and I can't say I'd blame 'em,' he'd told the boy. Oh, he could go through all the boys and know how they'd grow up; he could even tell which of the little girls would become totties in time.

Donovan always believed that the law should be tempered with mercy, and he dutifully practised his belief, as in the case of Viviana. Viviana was a totty, and a pretty young totty at that. She charged two shillings a time, and men came and went at all hours of the night and day. But something had to be done about it, and so he called on her in her little house in Munday Street between the workhouse and the Victoria Mill. He appreciated she had to earn money in order to live, he told her; and he could well see that the availability of tarts was an outlet for sinful men who might even rape little girls if they couldn't get what they wanted; so he told her he wouldn't arrest her if she would let him have her every Monday night. She saw no objection, for the gentlemen were always skint by Monday and there were never any customers.

Monday nights were definitely the best nights to rob a house in Ancoats, not that there was anything worth stealing, for Constable Donovan became a regular visitor; and they were happy together. She would laugh and call him 'Constable Don Giovanni' and he would correct her and say it was 'Donovan'. Then something difficult happened. He fell in love with her, genuinely in love with her; so much in love with her that he couldn't stop thinking about her. He asked her to marry him.

'But, *caro mio*, you know what I am,' she said, and tears rolled down her face. 'There is many men; many, many men. And we have a row some time, and you throw it up at me. Besides, we could not live here. Presto! Hey! You forget about love, eh—'

'I'm thinking of another country,' he said. 'Canada, where you make a fresh start, and nobody knows or cares what you was. I'll learn French, and I'll be a mounted policemen up in them Rocky Mountains. And we'll go to Niagara Falls. And isn't it all clean and fresh ye'll feel just looking at all that wonderful water come a-tumbling—'

She turned him down, but she said she loved him as much as he loved her. They found a lot of things to laugh and be happy about. She sang '*La donn' é mobile*', which he didn't understand a blessed word of, but she told him not to worry – she'd never be changeable. She bought him a pair of slippers, and he bought himself a book on learning French. When he made love to her, her face went smoother and smaller and she looked younger and younger.

It was either the knocker-up or the lamplighter, one of the two, who banged on Donovan's door one daybreak. Viviana had been found murdered in an entry. He felt elated as he ran through the streets because he knew it wasn't true, not at all. But it was true. She was lying in a twisted shape with her eyes wide open and her lips apart and her jet-black hair ruffling across her face. There were no shoes on her feet, and she'd been strangled with one of her own silk stockings. Her frock was above her knees, and her petticoat was showing. A group of mill women stood around and gazed down on the body.

'And will ye be weighing up that fancy lace on her petticoat? She never got that from no Woolworths,' said one woman.

'Cost a pretty penny, with all them fancy trimmings.'

'Ah well, there'll be no more pretty pennies for her ladyship, and that's for sure. Or was it shillings?'

'Give me a shilling and I'm willing,' giggled one of the younger women, and they all laughed.

'Her next man will be Old Nick himself, and I'm thinking he'll not be offering her a brass farthing for her favours.'

Donovan tried to get the women to part with one of their shawls to cover the body, but they clenched them; they weren't going to have an honest shawl draping a dead whore. He eventually found a length of dirty sacking which was covering a mangle in one of the backyards. As he knelt down to put the sacking over her, he felt his head was nigh bursting.

The day gave him the routine worries to contend with. A half-rotted dog had been found in the river. He knew the dog and the people who owned it, and they'd have to shift it. A woman came to him with her son who'd confessed to stealing money from Miss Daly's till. And somebody broke somebody's window. He wanted to hit them all.

That night, he had to go with a detective from house to house.

'Did you hear screams last night?'

'Aw sure! Don't we often hear screams? 'Tis usually some brassy little bitch getting what she deserves. We thought nothing of it.'

'Did you hear screams last night?'

'Oh, I did! And I said to me husband, "Play your bloomin' old mouth organ, Tom; let's not be mithered by all that fightin' going on in the entry."'

'Did you hear screams last night?'

'Well now, I thought 'twas a cat. Them damn moggie-moonlights'd wake up the dead, don't ye know?'

''Twas none of my business, and d'ye seriously think I'd risk going out in that entry in the dark and maybe getting me throat cut into the bargain by whoever it was?'

'Course I heard the screams; I'd be a liar to say I didn't. But stay out of it, Jack, says I to meself. Don't ye be getting yourself mixed up with the police, and it's their job to be hearing the screams the same as you, says I.'

Donovan walked the streets, not noticing the days becoming nights, and the nights turning into days. The only thing which stopped him weeping was his determination to find the murderer. About what seemed the third day he was walking up an entry to smoke a cigarette when he heard some kids talking in a backyard.

'When I grow up I'll kill that bobby,' said Michael. 'He says he can put me dad in prison whenever he has a mind to.'

'And didn't he help put me dad in Strangeways?' said Terence. 'I'll hold him while you kill him.'

'I'll drown him like he drowned Tiny,' said Sean.

'Perhaps he'll get fired for not finding the man who killed the tart,' said Kevin. 'I know who it was, but I wouldn't tell him 'cos they might make him a sergeant or summat, then he'd be ten times worser.'

With one voice the rest of the lads demanded to know who it was, promising not to tell the bobby on God's honour.

'The paper said she was done in about ten o'clock, didn't it? Well I was passing the entry on me way back from Auntie Bridget's about half-past nine and there was this feller going into the entry with a tart, and there was giggling in the dark.'

'I thought you said you knew who it was?'

'For don't I look through the windows of the Victoria Mill to watch the tarts on the looms? And isn't he the foreman with the brown coat and all them fountain pens in the pocket, and him always wearing a bowler hat?'

Donovan's first instinct was to charge into the yard. Then he thought for a second. Suppose the murderer was the man described – and the tecks would soon find out, once he'd tipped them off – then wouldn't it be a terrible thing for a young boy to have on his mind all his life that he'd got a man topped? Well, the kid would never know. 'Information received' was all he'd put in his report; and he'd taken the credit, or the blame, for the man being arrested for murder.

Donovan took a swig from his Guinness, drew on his cigarette and stared into the fire. His clock chimed. He knew the trapdoor had been jerked open and the murderer's neck would be snapped on the noose. It was all over. There was nothing more.

He grabbed the French book from the table and dropped it on the fire. There was a banging on the door. It was Kevin, the very boy he'd been thinking about, and it made him goose-pimple for a second.

'Come quick, master! There's a horse broke out of its stable, and it's hit a tram, and it's running like mad down Every Street.'

Although the small coffin in the hearse contained a boy from their own school, the children in the street continued playing and singing. It was the wedding game, which only the smaller children played. One boy had his sister's frock on, which made him a priest, and he blessed the couples who skipped up before him.

Finger to finger, thumb to thumb,
Belly to belly, bum to bum. Amen.

Further down the street, a kid was shouting through a door hole:

Tell-tale tit, your tongue shall be slit,
And all the little puppydogs will have a little bit.

And at the end of the street, two grown men were fighting with their fists. They were Seamas and Thomas Kennedy; they lived in a cellar; neither was married. The fight, which took place every week at much the same time, was about whether they should emigrate to Canada or Australia, for the one was all for the one country, and the other was all for the other. Being brothers, they never pulled their knives out. As the hearse rattled towards them, they stood to attention and made the sign of the cross. The gang, who had been watching the fight, ran away when the hearse came near for they didn't wish to make the sign of the cross.

'Where's Australia?' asked Sean.

''Tis a million miles away, and as far as the moon,' said Patrick.

'Sure 'tis no place for an Irishman to be going,' said Sean.

'I'd not say that,' said Kevin, 'for there's been some Irishmen become very famous in Australia.'

'Like who?'

'There was Ned Kelly, a more famous highwayman than Dick Turpin. And there was Jack Doogan, the wild colonial boy what was nearly as famous. They was both hanged.'

'Then why travel all them millions of bloody miles to get hanged, when you can stay in Ancoats and get hanged?'

'Then there's Don Bradman.'

'He doesn't sound Irish.'

'No, but I heard an Englishman saying he deserved bloody hanging.'

'What for?'

'For beating the English at cricket. They make you play cricket in Australia from a baby.'

'Then that lets us out,' said Terence. 'Micks isn't allowed to play cricket, Constable Donovan says.'

'Ach, ye blithering galoot, that's only micks in Ancoats 'cos of the windows,' said Kevin. 'If you was to score a hundred runs in the streets, it'd mean breaking a hundred windows, and that'd cost a thousand pounds.'

''Tis what I've always thought,' said Michael, 'cricket is a game for the rich.'

'Perhaps windows is cheaper in Australia?' said Terence.

'Ar, ye're hopeless cases,' sighed Kevin. 'Australia is a thousand times bigger than England, and the houses are a hundred miles apart. But I'll tell ye summat – I'll bet Don Bradman could hit a ball from one end of Australia to the other if he tried.'

'Only if the ball landed in the truck of a passing railway train,' said Michael.

'Trouble is,' said Patrick, 'you'd have to learn Australian if you was going to be a bold rapparee, for if you said "Stick 'em up" they'd not understand you and might just smile and carry on.'

'The most dangerous thing about Australia and Canada,' said Kevin, 'is their rivers, for they're teeming full of crocodiles and sharks and snakes and man-eating salmon.'

'Can't be more dangerous than the cut, with all them germs. I'll bet that kid going up the street in the box had been sniffing the Medlock.'

The trend of talk gave Kevin an idea. The gang could clean up the Medlock and save thousands of lives, and they could do it by putting soap in the water, for soap killed germs, and he was an expert on soap, with a certificate to prove it. There was general agreement on Kevin's plan, which was to put as much soap in the river as they could lay their hands on; Terence suggested the King might turn them into knights for doing it.

They began to steal soap from wherever soap was to be found; the cloakrooms of both schools, the lavatory at the Ragged School, the bucket cupboard in the Horsfall Museum, the school clinic, several mills, even the undertaker's. They were thrilled with the great soap hunt, and excited by the possibility of getting caught.

'I'm here 'cos the lice in me head is eating away at me brain,' Michael told the nurse when he was found in the clinic after hours.

'I thought you might be keeping a secret Gyptian mummy in the bucket closet,' Kevin told Mr Peg Leg when he was seen shutting the closet door.

'I wanted some of that special soap you clean dead bodies with,' Terence told Mr O'Rourke, 'for I know a dead body what hasn't been washed for nearly a fortnight.'

'' Twas on me mind that if I washed with the soap you use in the University Settlement, I might smell educated, if nowt else,' Sean told the young man with the long scarf.

Within a week they had gathered half a sack of soap, which they took to the bridge in Russell Street. Nobody would suspect it was stolen soap; they'd think it was a cat being taken to be drowned.

They dropped the pieces in one by one. They just plopped down through the rainbow-coloured rings of oil; nothing happened.

'Where do rivers go?' asked Patrick.

'Some of them go to the sea,' answered Kevin.

The gang walked away, disappointed. Then they saw Seamas and Thomas Kennedy walking down the road. They were on their way to emigrate, for they were wearing new caps, and men always bought or stole new caps to emigrate with. They also had one very large suitcase tied up with skipping-ropes, and they stopped every now and again to argue about who should carry the case. Once they stopped and sat on the suitcase back to back and smoked a cigarette, still not decided who should carry the case next.

'Have ye decided?' shouted Sean.

'Oh, we have that,' said Seamas. ''Tis for Australia we're bound, to shear the sheep.'

'And to find fame and fortune,' added Thomas.

'Aye, that as well,' said Seamas.

'Then 'tis careful ye'd best be,' said Patrick, 'for the blooming old ocean will be full of bubbles.'

As the boys walked away, the two men began threatening each other about carrying the suitcase, and it looked as though another emigration fight might be brewing.

'Sure, I don't know where it is they'll end up,' said Michael. 'But wherever it is, they'll never get there.'

The legend of Miss Daly – and some knew it to be true, and some knew it to be false – was that when she was a beautiful young girl in Kinsale she was in love with, and indeed was going to marry, a young fisherman. One day he confided in her that he was a member of the Irish Republican Army and was going to take part in an ambush. She was so worried about him that she told her father; for she had to have somebody to talk to, and who better than her father? What she didn't know was that her father was the leader of the local brigade of the IRA, and he was forced to execute the young fisherman for betraying the secret by putting a gun to his head. When Miss Daly found out, she stole the dowry which her dad had saved for her in a biscuit-tin and took the boat to England, where she bought the ingoing of the little general store in Tutbury Street; it seeming only right she should be selling biscuits seeing that the money had come from a biscuit-tin.

Every Sunday she wore the Kinsale cloak to Mass, which made her look like a nun in a black blanket. Some said it was in memory of her dead sweetheart. She was no longer young.

Miss Daly's shop was ideal for playing at ambushes; it could also represent New York for gangster fights. The lads weren't sure where New York was, except that it could be seen at the Palmy Picturedrome, and they'd been seeing and hearing a lot of

New York since Arthur had shown them the way to unlimited supplies of jam jars. During these games, they even talked 'picture talk', which was the slang of the gangsters. There were also 'picture kisses', which were long and lasting and wet; not a bit like the quick pecks on girls' cheeks down a back entry.

The shop stood by itself in Tutbury Street. There had once been a house on either side and at the back, but all that was left were scattered bricks on dust. The three houses which were once wall to wall with Miss Daly's had probably just collapsed and died in despair, rotting away with cancer of the mortar; maybe helped in their decay by the ever-present stink of strong cheese and paraffin firelighters which almost visibly spread from her shop. It was therefore perfect for ambushing, because unlike any other building in Ancoats it had four corners; Dutch Schultz could creep up on Legs Diamond not knowing that Lucky Luciano was also creeping up on him, and then there would be exciting gang-warfare with everybody rat-a-tat-tatting each other dead.

'The Duke of Wellington defeated Napoleon at the battle of Waterloo,' said Arthur, as the corpses were picking themselves up one afternoon. The rest of the lads stared at him as though he'd just come out with something very dirty.

'What made you say that?' asked Liam.

'It's what we're doing at school. Isn't it, Kevin?'

'You don't have to spoil a good gangster game by talking about school.'

'I just thought we could play at history for a change,' said Arthur meekly.

'Gangsters is history,' said Patrick. 'Or they will be some day, when they've conquered New York.'

'We could play at the IRA on the Fenian Arch,' said Liam. 'It's weeks since we played that.'

'I'm not playing IRA any more,' said Arthur. 'I'm always the policeman what gets killed.'

'That's because you're English,' said Liam. 'We couldn't play the game without you.'

'Why don't you be English once in a while, and let me be one of them what gets hanged by the neck and cheered?'

'Even in pretend, none of us could be English,' said Sean. 'It'd be a mortal sin.'

'I say we stick at gangsters,' said Patrick. 'It's best. Look,' he

71

went on, 'none of us'll ever be dukes or generals, so it's a waste of time playing it. But we might grow up to be famous gangsters.'

'I bet Legs Diamond doesn't know about the Duke of Wellington and Waterloo,' said Sean.

'He doesn't have to; he's rich. Yeh, dead rich,' said Liam.

'That's it, isn't it?' said Patrick. 'Dukes is born dukes and rich. But them gangsters was poor and baggyarsed like us, and came from places like us, and now they're millionaires. And they didn't get their money by learning history.'

'Or their catechism either,' added Michael.

'I don't know about that,' said Patrick. 'Most of them is Catholics and have very sacred and expensive motorcars with millions of flowers at their funerals. Being a gangster doesn't mean to say you can't believe in Jesus.'

All the lads except Arthur made a rapid sign of the cross.

'Who would you rather have?' asked somebody. 'Julius Caesar or Al Capone?'

'Al Capone!' the rest shouted.

'And who would you rather have?' shouted somebody else. 'Al Capone or. . . . er. . . . Alfred the Great?'

'Al Capone!'

'Knowing about Alfred the Great burning them cakes isn't going to get us out of Ancoats to them posh houses you see from the tram. Nobody's going to help us; nobody's going to give us anything. "Where you from?" they say. "Ancoats," you say. And they hold their snouts and say "pooh".'

'They wouldn't say "pooh" if there was a tommy-gun stuck up their bums.'

'No, they'd be frightened and fart and mess themselves.'

'Then we could say "pooh",' added Kevin. And they all laughed and held their noses. But Patrick didn't laugh.

'We're a gang, aren't we?' he asked. They all agreed.

'And we could be as tough as the Kennedy gang, couldn't we?' Again they all agreed.

'Well, let's stop playing at it, and do our first job, with me as boss.'

There was a silence. Somebody whispered that if it was horse muck through the letterboxes again they weren't interested. They were at the back of Miss Daly's shop, and Patrick jerked his thumb towards the wall.

'Her shop,' he said quietly.

'Miss Daly's?'

'Tuesday afternoon straight after school. Nobody goes in Tuesday afternoon 'cos it's the last day before public assistance and she won't give any more tick till the tick books are paid up on Wednesday. And isn't that always the way?'

'We'll get nabbed. We'll get locked up.'

'No, you won't. Leave it to me.'

There was a shuffling. Some turned to go home. One lad threw some stones at a pigeon; another pretended he was playing hopscotch and hopped about on one leg. Patrick grabbed each one by the shoulder and held his clenched fist under their noses.

'Am I the boss?' he demanded of them one by one. They all mumbled that he was.

'Then anyone who doesn't come with me on Tuesday gets his fingers trapped in a grid by the others till they're nearly hanging off.'

Miss Daly always took a long time to answer the bell on the curly spring; and she always apologized in her County Cork accent that she'd been having forty winks or a wee nap. To the gang on the Tuesday afternoon, it seemed she'd gone to bed for the night. They had filed into the shop with Patrick leading. They were frightened and didn't know where to look.

Kevin gazed at the six black blobs in the front of the window. A year ago they'd been pure white sugar mice with pink eyes and a string tail, but the summer sun through the glass had melted them, and the soot in the air had blackened them; they were the colour of snow after it had been in the street a couple of hours.

Michael stared at the faded Father Christmas which was drawing-pinned up on one of the shelves. This too had been in the shop a long time, two Christmases at least; and what had once been a red cap was now just a shade muckier than the beard.

Arthur concentrated on the strip of fly-catcher hanging down from the ceiling; it was nearly covered in last summer's flies. In the summer a couple of flies could always be seen struggling on it, and they were very interesting to watch. Miss Daly never changed the fly-catcher until there wasn't any room for another fly to die on.

Terence's attention was taken up by the gaslight; it was one of the wonders of the world. It had three gas mantles, not just one, and they didn't point upwards, like all gas mantles did, but downwards. There were two little chains – pull one to put the light on, pull the other to turn it off – and there was always a tiny blue flame burning. 'Miss Daly must be very rich to afford to keep a blue flame always burning just so she won't have to strike a match,' he thought.

'And remember,' had warned Patrick, 'use picture talk, for that'll make her wet her bloomers with fear.'

'Och, I'm sorry to have kept you waiting,' she said when she came out of the parlour. 'I was just resting my weary eyes. Now, what is it I can be doing for you?'

'Listen, dame,' said Patrick, 'we want some twopenny bars of chocolate. And we ain't got no dough, sister.'

'Then ye may get away out of my shop. Is it not my unbreakable rule that I do not give credit to children under no circumstances? Is it not your own mothers and fathers that have asked me to make sure the rule is carried out? So be away with ye all!'

'We're a gang, and we're going to put you on the spot and bump you off if you don't give us them chocolate bars.'

'And we're gonna take you for a ride and fill you full of holes,' added Kevin.

Miss Daly grabbed hold of her sweeping brush and raised it high. 'And I'll be smashing your head while you're doing it, that I will. Now, out ye go and play your games in the street, ye blithering little bunch of spalpeens, ye! Be off and pray for forgiveness now!'

'Sez you, baby!' said Patrick, and he picked an egg out of a bowl on the counter and let it drop on the floor. 'Aw gee, one of them eggs has got itself broke.'

Liam made a noise like a clucking hen, and flapped his arms. It relieved the tension amongst the boys, who flapped their arms and laughed.

Miss Daly sensed that a group of laughing boys could easily start to run wild. She put the broom down.

'Will ye listen now,' she said. 'I know all your mothers and fathers, and fine people they are, oh, fine people. Now if you leave my shop like young gentlemen I'll not be breathing a word to them. If ye don't, then it's round to your houses I'll be calling.'

'And if ye do, 'twill be bricks we'll be chucking through your window. Or maybe 'tis firelighters we'll be shoving through your letterbox at midnight, and burn your shop down. We're the shirt-tearers!'

'I'll tell Father Sullivan.'

'And if ye do, we'll chalk dirty words over all your walls, and people will blush to come in your shop.'

'I'll tell Constable Donovan.'

'I don't think you'll be telling Constable Donovan in a hurry,' said Patrick, with a sly confidence, 'for I heard a big man say that them cigarettes you've got on your shelves was stolen from Swan Street. And I can tell the bobby the name of the man I heard say it.'

'Look, children, I'm a poor woman as never so much as kept a cow in the old country,' appealed Miss Daly. 'Am I not just trying to keep body and soul together, like your own good parents?'

'If you're that poor, missus, why d'y'keep a blue gas flame burning like at church just so you can pull a chain and not go striking a match? Me mam and dad sometimes don't have pennies for the meter.'

'Shut up, wise guy!' said Patrick, for he felt his gang was softening up, particularly as some of them were edging towards the door. 'Okay, you palookas, let's go tell Constable Donovan what we know.'

'Ah, now just a minute, boys,' said Miss Daly, reaching chocolate bars from the shelf. 'I'm giving you these because your parents are good customers, and not because of anything you said about cigarettes, which isn't true, and may the Lord have mercy on your souls.'

'Oh, and a lucky bag as well,' said Patrick. 'One with a ring in it.'

She fumbled inside the cardboard box where the lucky bags were kept until she eventually handed one to Patrick. Then she started sniffling and sobbing and vigorously sweeping the floor.

The lads skipped out of the shop, whooping like wild Indians. They rushed down a back entry and stuffed the chocolate down their mouths as though they'd never had a bit to eat in all their born days.

'We had her on the spot,' said Patrick.

''Tis better than catching rats or selling funeral flowers,' said Sean. 'Hey, next time we could make her give us money.'

'I'm not taking money,' said Michael. 'That'd be stealing. And anyway, why did you take that lucky bag extra? Us Communists believe in share and share alike.'

'We're not Communists, for Communists are dead evil. We're gangsters and I'm the gangster boss, and every boss has to have a moll, and the ring in the lucky bag is for my moll, who is Vera, and that's only fair.'

Then he took the ring out of the lucky bag, tipping the powdered kali over Arthur's head like snow. He studied the ring. ''Tis only tin,' he said. 'Maybe I ought to get her summat better, like gold or that.'

Betty had never been outside the black crawling triangle of Ancoats, but Kevin to some extent had seen the world; at least he'd seen a great deal of Manchester with his father taking him to different churches every Sunday.

'Ah!' his dad would say when they left the house each Sunday morning, 'we're a couple of artful dodgers, you and me. We've beaten this blooming old excommunication from Saint Anne's, right enough.' And his dad would tap down his bowler with a pride of achievement. Sometimes they had to set off very early when the church his dad picked was the other side of town. Thus Kevin's mind was broadened, and he got to know the names of saints he never knew existed, like Kentigern, Edward, Edmund, Boniface, Augustine and Wilfrid, as well as The Holy Name and The Hidden Gem. As they invariably went to eleven o'clock Mass, which finished at twelve when the beerhouses opened, his father too learned a lot of new names, like the Grapes, Dog and Partridge, Robin Hood, Wagon and Horses, and Ben Brierley. Kevin told Betty all about his travels, but she was more interested in trees, and asked him to talk about trees. 'For I've never seen a tree in all my life,' she told him.

He loved her all the more because she'd never seen a tree; he wanted to give her a token of his love, but, like Patrick with Vera, felt that a lucky-bag ring wasn't enough. Then he thought of something which made him so excited he couldn't sleep; it involved the Horsfall Museum and the help of Arthur. The whole idea seemed divine.

He prepared himself by spending a lot of time in the museum, usually counting the square tiles on the floor because it seemed a clever thing to do. Even the air inside the museum had a clever smell, with just a whiff of disinfectant. Schools had only half-clever smells mingled with chalk, but the museum had a full-clever smell. He took deep breaths of it, and he walked around on tiptoe and gave little coughs in order to sound interested.

One of the ground-floor rooms by the side of the shunting yard was an aviary with ten budgerigars in a large mesh enclosure, and a map saying they came from Australia. Around the walls, to remind people they were in Manchester, were framed pictures of old Manchester, although hadn't they only to look through the windows? But on the floor inside the aviary – ah yes – was a concrete birdbath, and attached to it a two-foot-high cupid, all naked and with everything showing which a boy without trousers would show. Cupid had a pair of wings on his shoulders and a bow and arrow in his hand. Mr Peg Leg never allowed boys and girls to go into the bird room at the same time; they invariably giggled at Cupid and had to be pushed out. Terence had told Kevin the statue was called Cupid and it was the god of love, whose mother was also bare but had no arms.

'All I'm asking from you, Arthur, is to get Mr Peg Leg to show you the Roman coins.'

People had to ask to be shown these coins because they were kept locked up in the office so that nobody would steal them for the gas-meter or the cigarette machines.

'Then while he's showing them to you, I'll sneak into the bird room and get in the cage and knock Cupid's thingummy off with me ruler.'

'What for?'

'To give to Betty, ye daft ha'porth. 'Tis the kind of thing they did in good King Arthur's day, and you should know, being named after him. They were made knights for doing it.'

Arthur asked to see the coins.

'What d'y'want to see 'em for?' asked Peg Leg.

'Because I like looking at money.'

'So do I. Every Friday.'

'I mean money what's been found and not stolen.'

'Why? Have you seen stolen money?'

'No, Mr Peg Leg. And chocolate isn't the same.'

'Come on then. And don't call me Peg Leg, I can't help me

77

wooden leg. That was done by Johnny Turk at Gallipoli for King and country.'

Meanwhile, Kevin slipped into the bird room, opened the cage door, and crept among the budgerigars who seemed to be discussing it. Then they stopped chatting and watched him. He pulled the ruler from his stocking and took a sharp swipe at Cupid's thingummy. It fell off, plop, into the water. He snatched it and put it in his pocket. But immediately, all the birds panicked and flapped and fluttered and banged and crashed. Most went straight through the open cage door and zigzagged around the room. One tried to land on a picture and sent Manchester Cathedral swinging and swaying. They squawked, squeaked and chirped.

Kevin tried to reason with them. 'Shut up, ye daft little buggers,' he hissed. He opened the window and escaped on to the railway embankment with the intention of clambering down into Palmerston Street.

A pigeon fluttering between the railway lines attracted his eye. He crossed the tracks to it. The pigeon had damaged its wing and was rolling and writhing on the oily gravel and sleepers. If he left it there, a shunting engine would sooner or later go over it. If he took it home, somebody would pull its neck out and eat it, for in a district where they drowned sick dogs, put cats down the grid, and kittens down the lavatory, the only treatment for a poorly pigeon was to have its neck screwed round.

He picked it up as carefully as he could and took it to the museum window. He pushed the pigeon through, closed the window, and scrambled down the embankment. It was pure cleverness, he told Arthur later; for both Miss Hindshaw and Mr Peg Leg would think the pigeon had sneaked in, let the birds out of the cage, and in the struggle had damaged its wing and snapped Cupid's thingummy off, which it had swallowed because everybody knows a pigeon pecks at stones. And Miss Hindshaw, being Miss Hindshaw, would forgive the pigeon and nurse it and make it better, so it could fly away from Ancoats to the countryside where there were trees.

Before school bell next morning, Kevin twisted Betty's arm behind her back and forced her into a corner of the playground, which was in the cellar of the school. He pushed the piece of plaster in her hand.

'What is it?'

He whispered in her ear. ''Tis the genuine thingummy belonging to the statue of the boy with no clothes on in the bird room of
the museum, and it's better than a tin ring from a lucky bag, and it
means I love you. I know it's not a tree, but perhaps it's like an
acorn, and if you plant it, it might grow into summat big.'

'I fink it's a dirty fing!' she yelled. 'And you're filfy and you stink
like a dead rat in a blocked drain.' And she ran off across the
playground to where seven of her friends were skipping in the
long skipping rope.

I'll tell me ma when I get home,
The boys won't leave the girls alone.

Later that day the gang walked into Miss Daly's. She gave them
bars of chocolate without saying a word.

'And a lucky bag with a ring in it,' demanded Patrick.

'And I want one too,' said Kevin.

'In that bloomin' case we all want lucky bags,' said Sean. 'But it
doesn't matter whether they've rings or not.'

'Now you boys understand I'm only giving you these because
none of your fathers ever misses eleven o'clock Mass,' she said.

'Here,' said Kevin, putting a round piece of plaster on the
counter, 'this is for you, Miss Daly.'

'And what, if I may ask, would it be?'

''Tis a piece of stone brought back from the sacred hill of the
Holy Land where our Blessed Saviour was crucified, died and
was buried. And it's been blessed by His Holiness the Pope.'

'We'll live for ever!' The gang, arms joined behind their backs,
skipped round the corner form Palmerston Street into Tutbury
Street; then they stopped. They couldn't remember which street
the dead man was in. Some were of the opinion it was Fleetwood
Street; others thought it was Napier Street. It was a pity, for none
of them had had breakfast, which was usually bread and jam, and
they'd been looking forward to the cake and ginger beer. They
stood and stared and thought.

It was a typical Saturday morning. As always, the trains
were shunting and pooping and clanging in the goods yard. A

chimneysweep walked up the street, carrying his brushes over his shoulders, and shouting 'Sweeee – eeeep!' He was black with soot, and must have slept that way. A mill girl touched him for luck, then ran back in the house. A scissor-grinder had set up his wheelbarrow and was treadling sparks from his big wheel. 'Any knives to grind? Knives to grind?' The ragboneman, with his donkey and cart, rattled down the street, blowing his bugle and shouting, 'Eeeeyagbone!' Somewhere in Dunn Street 'Selections from the Italian Operas' was playing on the barrel-organ. In Garden Place the girls were, as ever, singing their skipping-rope songs.

> *Pulled my hair and stole my comb,*
> *But I'll not care when I get home.*

A man in a dirty old raincoat with a row of medals pinned on it turned into Tutbury Street. He trundled up the gutter, sometimes walking forward, occasionally walking backward. There was a card around his neck which said 'Disabled'. He began singing, or it was more like shouting, 'I wish I was in Carrickfergus'. He stopped and slowly but loudly blew his nose on a dirty rag, 'Or else in Antrim or Ballygrange'. There was a pause while he pinned back a medal which was falling off, 'But the sea is wide and I cannot swim over'. Here he stopped for a minute and cleaned his boots with the same rag he had wiped his nose on, 'Nor have I wings so's I might fly'.

'It says "disabled",' said Michael, 'but he's got two arms and two legs and he isn't blind, so what's disabled about him?'

'Perhaps it's his voice,' said Kevin. 'The Germans must have done summat to it.'

Two young women strolled down the street singing 'She's a Lassie from Lancashire'. Ancoats was very noisy.

Constable Donovan rumbled down the street on his bicycle. He seemed to read the lads' minds. ''Tis Napier Street ye'll be wanting,' he shouted at them, and rang his bell.

They prayed over the body, and stuffed the cake in their mouths, then went out in the street again to discuss going to the Palmy for the kids' matinee. Terence announced that he'd been given permission not to go. 'For haven't I seen the same picture every night this week,' he explained; which wasn't really an explanation, for the true explanation was that a man had started calling on his mother every evening, and the man had given him his picture money and told him not to come back home until ten o'clock. It was still nippy in the evening, and Terence had been forced to go to the Palmy to keep warm. He'd once come home early, but the door had been bolted and the man's voice shouted for him to sod off.

The lads asked him what the picture was about; they didn't want to waste jam jars on anything sissie like people kissing each other. He told them it was about the war and this man got into an aeroplane and went up in the sky to shoot a Zeppelin down, but he didn't know whether he shot it down or not, for he always went to sleep at that point and didn't wake up until the crowds were rushing out of the picturedrome before the gramophone played 'God Save the King'.

He wished his dad would hurry up back out of prison. Perhaps if he could save up money and buy his mother a piano, she would be happy polishing the piano and not want to be bothered with the man.

Terence thought an opportunity to earn money had come when he heard the same afternoon that there was a job going. Taffy the milkman wanted a milk boy, for seven mornings a week, from half past four until half past seven. It was simply jumping off the cart and ladling milk from the churns into the jugs on the doorsteps. The pay was three shillings a week.

Mr Taffy talked in a strange sing-song sort of way, which Terence thought was Cork, and Sean insisted was Waterford; but it was in fact the dialect of Wales. Taffy and his wife had left Wales for ever after his father and two brothers had been buried alive in a pit disaster in the Rhondda Valley.

The trouble was that Sean also wanted the job. His dad was an out-of-work, but his mother did some drudging at a posh district which needed a long tram ride. The pay was very low because she was permitted to bring home leavings from the plates as well as dog food, for the people she drudged for kept greyhounds. She mixed the dog food into a pan with the leavings, and made a hash which she called 'medlars for pedlars'. They had this every day, and Sean developed a craving like an illness for fish and chips with lots of salt and vinegar. It was his stomach which wanted the job as a milk boy.

'Very difficult it is to choose between you,' Taffy told them, 'both of you being such bright young sparks, and both of you looking as if you could hop around in the early morning like little dickie-birds. Look now, suppose you both go away and fight it out? How's that now? And whichever is the winner turns up at the milk platform in the goods yard on the dot of four-thirty this very Monday morning.'

The fight was arranged for Saturday evening on the Dunn Street croft, and it was to be a big fight, and was to be known as 'the milk boys fight'. Dozens of boys and girls gathered on the croft, Catholics and Protestants, for there was no religious bigotry involved when a good private fight took place. Men and women peeped through the nettings of their bedroom windows; they dared not allow themselves to be seen peeping lest it be said they should have stopped the fight.

The only grown-up on the croft was the Mighty Mulligan. In his younger days, the Mighty Mulligan had been a street fighter at sixpence a fight and the cock o' the walk, until his opponent had shredded him with six-inch nails in his fists and almost stopped him from being a Mulligan any more. Now he contented himself by serving as a referee in any official street fight between man and man, boy and boy, woman and woman, or woman and man; taking twopence each from the contestants for the expenses of first-aid treatment, which was usually dipping a rag in the nearest puddle and dabbing the badly cut parts.

'No dirty fighting!' said the Mighty Mulligan. 'I'll be wanting no dirty fighting! D'y'hear that now? And there'll be no bad feeling so which one wins or loses.'

The two lads got themselves into the spirit of hatred by shouting a few things at each other.

'Your dad's a jailbird, and your mam does it for her fancyman every night,' shouted Sean.

'And everybody in your house eats what dogs have left. And you drownded your dog so you could eat its food!' yelled Terence.

Terence kicked Sean between the legs. As Sean doubled up in pain, Terence swung his elbow up into his face with a loud crack. Sean put his hands to his face, and Terence kicked both shins with all the swing and force of a footballer. Sean dropped to the ground. 'Make a fight of it!' shouted some of the boys. 'Take his trousers down,' shouted some of the girls. Terence kicked Sean

82

in the back, and jumped on top of him, thumping and thumping him. There were cheers from the crowd. The people in the windows forgot discretion and moved the nettings aside to get a clearer view. Mighty Mulligan lit a cigarette. In these two beloved boys he was well pleased.

They rolled over and over on top of each other. Terence put his knee in Sean's belly and twisted his arm behind his back, pushing and pushing to get Sean's arm higher; and everybody hushed, waiting to hear the crack of a broken shoulder; but Sean spat in his opponent's face, causing him to slacken the pressure. Sean wriggled his arm free and rolled on top of Terence, putting a knee on each shoulder; he then bounced his backside like a ton weight on Terence's belly. The situation was a deadlock; all they could do was spit into each other's faces and threaten each other that there was consumption in their spit. But luck was with Sean. His hand found a piece of broken roof slate. He tried to stab Terence in the face with it, but Terence managed to grip his wrist, and it became a trial of bulging muscle and quivering arm.

'Will ye be surrendering?' panted Sean. 'Or I'll be scraping scratches on your mug till ye'll be needing a thousand stitches.'

'Mr Mulligan!' screamed Terence. 'He's fighting dirty!'

The Mighty Mulligan puffed his chest out, and strutted before the crowd like a victorious gorilla.

''Tis a fair fight,' said he. 'And 'tis not as if he'd come into this arena carrying or concealing a deadly weapon. That slice of slate was left lying there on God's good earth by nature itself. And who'll be disputing with the Mighty Mulligan?'

'I surrender,' gasped Terence. Sean jumped to his feet and helped Terence up.

'Begod,' said Sean, 'if ye fight like that when you're a priest, ye'll be having them Protestants lining up to be converted.'

The two lads put their arms around each other and went along to Arthur's to get a wash before going to confession.

Mr Taffy sang out at the top of his voice as the two-wheeled horse and cart with its milk churns turned out of the goods depot; Sean was excited. It was his first morning on the milk round. It was too early for the mill chimneys to smoke; the air was crisp and the stars were sparkling. Taffy sang, and Sean liked the song; it was like a song from his own country, yet it wasn't an Irish song. It was sad, but it didn't make you want to cry.

Or in the soft noontide in solitude wander
Among the dark shades of the lonely ash grove.

Mr Taffy first called home to put water in the milk churns. He explained to the boy that water must always be added to milk because milk straight from the cow was too strong for the ordinary stomach to take; he made Sean promise never to tell the secrets of the profession. But there was, to Sean, one big snag to the job; it was a snag which he knew he'd have to face up to; and the snag was called Dobbin.

He was afraid of getting to know animals because he became too fond of them; and whenever he got fond of an animal it seemed to die. He did not want to know about animals. He hated animals. And now there was this thing pulling the cart. It was a proud young horse, but as far as Sean was concerned it was a 'thing'; just a thing which moved, and made two wheels which were taller than the cart itself roll over the cobbles.

The thing automatically stopped and started every twenty yards up and down and around the streets. For the first few days, Mr Taffy didn't allow him to dip for the milk, and Sean ran alongside the wheels, picking up the jugs and taking them to Mr Taffy, who dipped his long-handled tin into the churn and ladled out twopence three-farthings or threepence three-farthings of milk; then the boy put the beaded cloth covers back on the jugs and returned them to their doorsteps.

'Why do they do milk in farthings?' he asked.

'Oh, that's a question and a half now, isn't it?' said Mr Taffy. 'And the answer, boy, is very plainly and simply that it is the decision of the King of England who makes the laws for us to obey, and it has nothing whatsoever to do with me or you or the moo-cows in the meadow.'

He soon got to know all the jugs; it was a morning world of jugs. He no longer thought of people living in the houses, but of tall white jugs which were snobbish and thought they were special, fat little brown jugs which seemed as if they wanted to laugh, green jugs with gold rims which might have danced if jugs could dance, cracked jugs sorry for themselves, jugs with plain handles like the arms of girls, jugs with ornamental handles which were grand-mothers. Jugs had milk for breakfast, and when they got back in their houses they would laugh and talk with teapots and sugar bowls; or maybe the teapots were the bosses and would say to the jugs 'go out and spend the night on the steps, and don't come in again until you've got some milk'. Some of the jugs would carry beer during the day, and would sit on brownstoned or whitestoned steps and get drunk, but they'd be washed spick and span for the morning milk. A jug always had to very clean, for it would be seen by other jugs. A jug never talked to a plate.

Oh, but the air of Ancoats was beautiful before the mills of morning, and the stars twinkled almost blue with bursting eagerness.

'Isn't this the time of day to be alive and kicking?' said Mr Taffy. 'Smell the air, smell it, boy! When the wind comes down Every Street it is from the Pennine Chain; when it comes up Palmerston Street it is straight down the Ship Canal from Liverpool and the Irish Sea; when it blows up Tutbury Street it is from Snowdon and the singing valleys of Wales. There are times, boy, when I think I hear the blackbirds whistling.'

'Extra in the blue jug, Mr Taffy, because the note says there's been a death.'

'Then the hooters blow and the big chimneys wake up and puff their black rolling smoke into the sky, and the air is suffocated, and the stars get lost and cry for their mammies.'

Always at the bottom of Tutbury Street they met the knocker-up. He was the ugliest man Sean had ever seen. There were gashes and scars all over his face; one corner of his mouth was twisted almost to his nose, and brown teeth showed; one of his eyes wouldn't move. Sean knew that girls would run away from him. He himself had to turn away.

'Borrer-die!' shouted Mr Taffy every morning, and the knock-er-up neither looked nor answered but slithered along the street tapping at bedroom windows.

'Old Shagnasty doesn't like people,' said Mr Taffy. 'He goes to bed and stays there, once he's got them up and off to the mills.'

Sean picked up the round very fast. The sad thing was that he was caned every day at school for falling asleep in class, and his marks for all subjects were rarely more than 'two out of ten. See me.'

He remained annoyed by the thing which pulled the cart, and he didn't see why people had to leave it things like lump sugar, toast-crusts and carrots on the doorsteps, which only caused it to step on the pavement for them.

Then came a morning when fog was heavy. There was no Mr Taffy or horse and cart at the depot, and he had to find his way to the milkman's house and stable. Mrs Taffy was waiting, and she'd put the thing between the shafts.

'My husband has had such a temperature all night that you could have fried sausages in a pan on his bottom,' she said. 'In bed he is, and sweating like a little piggy-porker. Do you think you could take the round on your own just this once? The fog is lifting, and it will soon be as bright as a buttercup, you'll see.'

'Easily,' said Sean.

The churns were loaded at the depot, and with a flick of the reins and a 'giddy-up', boy, wheels, cart and thing rumbled towards Every Street.

But the fog wasn't lifting; the fog was thickening, and it tasted bitter as though vinegar was being poured through his nose into his lungs. It became so black and dense that he couldn't even see what was pulling the cart, but the cart continued to clatter its iron rims over the cobbles. Just occasionally a fog signal banged a muffled bang. There were no other sounds.

Sean trembled with a thousand fears. A tram or bus might smash into him; they might topple over into the river or the canal and drown, like a horse and cart had done in the Ship Canal some weeks before; they might drop into the ruins of the haunted church and be eaten by rats; they might be slammed by a shunting engine where the tracks crossed the road; they might keep going to the Pennines and stagger down a steep mountain, or rumble all the way to Wales and fall down a coal mine, down, down, down. He wanted to jump off the cart and leave it there and go home. But he couldn't; something seemed to keep his feet to the cart boards. He wished Terence had won the fight.

The cart stopped. He got off. There was the thing putting its mouth to a carrot. But there also were the jugs, the first jugs of the round. The wheels rattled over the stones; rattled and stopped, rattled and stopped. And the jugs were there waiting in their proper order. He had never been so happy to see jugs! The cart must have turned corners into the different streets, but it was impossible to tell; all he knew was that the poor old cracked white jug would come next, and it did, with a toast crust; and the jolly little brown jug would come next, and it did, with a lump of sugar.

Then he heard the tap-tapping of the knocker-up. 'Borrerdie!' he shouted.

'Is that you, Dobbin?' came the reply.

'No, it's not Dobbin. It's me, Sean, the milk boy.'

'I never talk to human beings,' said the voice, 'so it must be you, Dobbin. You're the only thing that ever looks at me without then looking away. How are you, Dobbin?'

'Very well, thank you, Mr Shagnasty.'

'I've never had chance to talk to you before, have I, Dobbin?'

'No.'

'Would you like me to tell you why I'm so ugly?'

'No.'

'But I'd like to tell you, because you're not afraid of looking at me.'

'All right, then!'

'I was still in the army when the English invaded Afghanistan in 1919, and although I'd got medals for fighting in Flanders field, this was different. It was hot and there was no water and the Afghans shot at you from behind rocks, then ran away. Three of us was captured and they stretched us out on boards. Jimmy was skinned alive, and he was screaming, and his red raw flesh was like in a butcher's shop only it was still bubbling and throbbing and pulsing. Then they cut Charlie's nose off, and his ears, and other things, and they jabbed red-hot pokers on his eyes. Then they started cutting me all over with their long curved knives. And I told them where my patrol was, and they let me crawl away, and I crawled and crawled. And I came to a place where all my patrol had had their heads chopped off, and 'twas me as had betrayed 'em. So you see, Dobbin, I don't want to see human beings ever again 'cos I know what human beings can be like. And what's more, Dobbin, there's an Afghan following me, and every morning he follows me with his curved knife to finish me off. I can't see him and you can't see him, but he's always creeping, and even if you look round quickly he'll dodge round a corner. Thank you for listening to me, Dobbin.'

The tapping started again; the ugly man moving off. And Sean, whose fears had been falling away until then, became more scared

87

than ever. Maybe Shagnasty had been lying; maybe he hadn't; but, whatever, he'd left the boy with a vivid picture image of an evil, bloodthirsty Afghan who might spring on to the cart and cut his throat slowly with a curved knife.

But then, he thought to himself, the horse would gallop him to safety if an Afghan tried to skin him alive. His confidence returned, and there was a distinct speeding-up of the horse. The mill and factory hooters began to howl, and would continue howling to guide workers through the fog. The day had begun. He had delivered their milk, and the knocker-up had risked being cut up by an Afghan to get them out of bed in time to earn their wages.

The horse stopped at the stable. Sean jumped off the cart, flung his arms around the horse's neck, and kissed its nostrils.

'Oh, Dobbin, Dobbin, Dobbin! You're a lovely horse! You're a great, brave, clever horse; you could win the Grand National if you wanted to. Alexander the Great never had such a good horse as you. I love you, Dobbin! I'll never let you carry cotton.'

He told the gang about it that night. They linked arms and lifted their knees high to strut in the middle of the street.

All the monkeys in Belle Vue have their backsides painted blue,
So, horsie, keep your tail up, keep your tail up, keep your tail up.
Horsie, keep your tail up. Keep the sun out of my eyes.

Arthur had sworn on God's honour to Betty that Kevin had rescued an injured pigeon just three feet away from the Flying Scotsman which had been coming at him at one hundred miles an hour through the Ancoats shunting yard; and she had therefore forgiven Kevin for being a dirty thing. In fact, Kevin was going to her house after Sunday dinner to show her his collection of broken lead soldiers. He'd told her how they'd come from the middens; and he even told her how, as a little boy when he believed in Father Christmas, he'd always imagined that somewhere in Lapland Father Christmas had a lot of gnomes working for him throughout the year, and their job was to smash toys up for him to get in his pillowcase.

Kevin was glad of the chance to call on Betty, because it was May Sunday and a very religious day which he wanted to avoid. It was the day when the children of Saint Anne's walked through the streets of the parish with the band playing and the banners waving; then they would pack the church and a girl would be crowned Queen of the May; and they would all sing, '*Mary, we crown thee with blossoms today, Queen of the angels, and Queen of the May.*' This year he would not be allowed to take part in the scholars' walk.

The Italians would be doing the same thing; only they would be carrying their huge Madonna covered in real lilies, and be led by MacSweeney's Pipe band, which wasn't fair for the Italians weren't Irish. Patrick had told him that Vera's dad was one of the lucky Italians who had been picked to help carry the Madonna; but this, as Patrick knowingly explained, was because her dad had joined the 'raffia'. Now, raffia was something with which infants made teapot stands in their early classes, and Patrick and Kevin assumed the Italians had formed a special society of those who had woven raffia mats together when young.

His day had begun by going with his dad to the church of The Holy Name. He liked this church because there was a statue of Joan of Arc in it; and, after all, wasn't she made a saint for being a heretic and fighting the English? And she didn't hold a lamb or a book or a string of rosary beads – she gripped a sword. He felt he could talk to her, and that day he plucked up enough courage to put something in the candle box and light a candle to her.

His father grabbed his arms as they left church.

'Where did ye get that coin for the candle from? Come on now, the truth!'

'It wasn't a coin,' he told his dad. 'It was a curtain ring.'

'Ye've set me mind at ease,' sighed his dad, relieved. 'For a moment I thought 'twas money ye'd pinched from yer mam's purse; and her refusing me the price of a pint.'

He shared a sheep's head with his father after Mass; it was something he didn't relish, but he didn't like to hurt his dad's feelings, it being bad enough for his dad being excommunicated, and that. Betty and her mam had eaten their Sunday dinner by the time he called, and the table had been sided away.

When Betty's father arrived, Kevin had the surprise of his life. Her dad had a round face, round ears and a round nose. On top of his round head he wore a polished black bowler; his clothes were black, and around his waistcoat he had a large orange sash. He

89

wore white gloves, and carried a stick. All these he took off gently, like a priest disrobing, and handed them to his wife, who carried them into the scullery with great care. The man sat down at the table, and she brought in a sheep's head on a plate.

'You'll be sharing it with me,' he said, handing Kevin a fork. 'And we'll be cutting the brains in half; half for you, half for me.' The man had a strong manner about him, and Kevin was afraid to say no. He knew the meal would go on until only a skull remained on the plate. They both began picking away with their forks.

'So you're the little redneck Betty's been telling me about? Little left-footer, eh?'

'Only half,' said Kevin. 'Me mam's a Protestant.' The thought flashed through Kevin's mind that there couldn't be much difference between Catholics and Protestants if they both ate sheep's heads.

'Ah,' said the man, obviously trying to catch Kevin out, 'but I suppose you stick up for Manchester United football team, eh?'

'No, master,' answered Kevin. 'I like Manchester City to win as well.' It was a tactful answer, and the man smiled.

'You looked surprised to see me in my regalia,' he said. 'Well now, 'tis a member of the Orange Order I am. I'm an Orange-man.' Then he prodded Kevin. 'You gotta show 'em, lad. Ah yes, you gotta show 'em.' He brandished his fork like a sword, with a piece of meat on it; he banged his other hand on the table:

For happy homes, for altars free, we grasp the ready sword;
For freedom, truth, and for our God's unmutilated word;
These, these, the watch-cry of our march – our hope the Lord on
*   high –*
Then put your trust in God, my boys, and keep your powder dry.

Kevin liked Betty's father, but he was a little frightened of him too. He set the broken lead soldiers on the table, and her dad was more interested in them than she was; in any case she was busy washing the pots in the scullery. He seemed to know as much about the regiments as his own dad; he talked about the Irish Guards at Mons just like his dad did.

When the sheep's head was finished, Kevin had to run off, wanting to wee down an entry, for he daren't ask to use their lavatory. Besides, he'd promised to meet Arthur in Great Ancoats

Street after Arthur had been let out of Sunday School. But before he left, he promised Betty he would take her to Platt Fields when it became summer; Platt Fields was full of real trees, and they all got on well together, and you couldn't look at the sun because it would blind you.

Arthur was waiting near the railway stables. He handed Kevin an old and tattered book which he said had been published in 1876.

'Then it's second-hand, and not worth a penny. Sides, people with all sorts of deadly diseases could have handled it; there could be measles and mumps and all sorts of things between the pages. Did it fall off the ragbone cart?'

'No, I got it this afternoon at Sunday School for a prize. Well, not really as a prize, but everyone else got new Bibles for knowing all about God, and answering questions.'

'That's daft, Arthur. There's no one can answer questions about God except God himself, and I'm not sure he can answer all the questions, at that. For with no mam and dad, and no missus, and no school, and no church, there must be times when he says to himself, "Who am I? And what the hell am I supposed to do now that I'm here?" I bet even God wouldn't get a Bible for answering questions about himself.'

'I asked the vicar if I could have a book, same as the rest of 'em, and he said he couldn't give me a Bible 'cos that was against the rules. So he gave me this one, which he forked out from his desk, and he told me a bit about it. It's called *The Manchester Man*.'

'I can see that.'

'There's this baby what gets washed up in a cradle when the Irk is in flood, and ends up at grammar school.'

'Ah, ye galoot! Ye daft piecan! The Irk goes nowhere near the grammar school, and they don't take wet babies.'

'There's killings in it as well. It's about Peterloo, which is Peter Square, and millions of poor people was killed by millions of soldiers on millions of horses because they was hungry.'

'Who was hungry? The poor people, the soldiers, or the horses?'

'All of them, I think. Anyway, the first man what got himself shot dead was right here in Great Ancoats Street, so I thought you and me could look for the bloodstains.'

'Sure you want your head seeing to! The soot will have covered the blood up by now. 'Sides, there's new bloodstains every Saturday night when the beerhouses let out. And, anyway, reading books is dangerous.'

'Give over.'

'I'm telling you. Reading makes your eyes go blind. Look at that tart what runs the library; she wears tortoise-shell glasses because of all them books, and will ye tell me what bloody use you'd be in a fight if you was wearing glasses? And who wants to read about Ancoats? Don't we live in the bloody place and all? And you can see a real live dead body any day, and get cake and ginger beer for doing it, without reading about it. Here, give it me. I'll save ye from it.'

Kevin was about to force it between the bars of a grid when he saw a scruffy old tramp crawling his way to Thames Street workhouse and tramp ward. In the bat of an eyelid he handed the book to the tramp. 'Here,' he said, ''tis summat ye can be reading while you're waiting.'

'Kiss me bum!' said the tramp, snatching it and stuffing it into an old army side-pack.

'What I've done is called charity, Arthur; and it's summat you don't do by singing hymns and trying to answer questions what even God can't answer.'

'Aye, but we won't ever get rich by giving things away.'

Kevin wrinkled his forehead and scratched his head to show he was thinking. Occasionally he put his head on one side. Then he straightened up and unwrinkled his brow to show that he had thought. 'Maybe not,' he said, 'but 'tis rich we'll be getting all the same, you and me. I've had me thinking cap on.'

'And?'

'You and me, we'll join the Boy Scouts in that hut at the University Settlement. And I'll tell you why. 'Tis because they learn you things like living in tents, tying knots, making fires from rubbing sticks, and boiling potatoes; and you get a knife for killing bears with. Then, when we're fully trained in them things, we'll be able to go to Canada digging for gold; 'tis called "prospering". There was an uncle of mine went off to Canada to dig for gold, only he's in prison now for driving a truck-load of whisky over the border into the United States of America.'

'Had he been in the Boy Scouts?'

'Of course he had.'

'Me mam said you could stay for tea.'

'It's not a sheep's head, is it?'

'No.'

'All right then. Only if I have another sheep's head I'll be growing wool and saying "baa".'

It was a great tea, with chips and bread with yellow butter on. But there was even a greater treat for Kevin. Arthur's mother came downstairs, and she was wearing a very tight black frock; it stopped several inches above her ankles, and the frill didn't start at her waist, but somewhere halfway down her legs. She wore a velvet hat, but it wasn't really a hat, not with a brim, but more like a cap which fitted tight to her head, one side of it coming down to her ear. She had bright red lipstick, and matching circles of rouge on her cheeks. There was a very long string of Woolworths pearls hanging from her neck to her belly. She had a wonderful sweet smell about her. Suddenly she began to dance and sing the 'Black Bottom', kicking her legs up backwards and touching her shoes with her hand; she swung the string of pearls until they hummed like a spinning top; she hopped and she jerked and she bounced; sometimes she sang 'Coochy-coo, coochy-coo, coochy-coo!'

Oh, this washed all the religion out of Kevin's mind, and on a Sunday evening too; May Sunday in fact, and what d'y'think of that?

She kissed Arthur good-night, in case she didn't come home before bedtime. Even when she'd gone, Kevin could see, hear and feel her dancing the 'Black Bottom'; and religion came back to him, but only because he thought of Arthur's mam with the lines of *'Mary, we crown thee with blossoms today; Queen of the angels, and Queen of the May.'*

'Sure you've got a wonderful mam,' he told Arthur.

'I know that. She's the best mam in the world.'

'Aye. But 'tis a pity she never made you wipe your snotty nose when it runs. Where's them hankies what cost me a lot of money at Christmas? Charity is wasted on you, Arthur.'

In Michael's considered opinion, Patrick had got the idea of Mussolini from the Jersey Street Italians; Patrick seemed to think that Mussolini was solving the problems of the poor in Italy by making them wash and sing, and by making them wear clean shirts and putting them on bicycles. Michael preferred to think of Karl Marx. Mr Marx wouldn't make people put clean shirts on every day and ride about the streets on bicycles singing jolly songs, unless they particularly wanted to. He saw Karl Marx as one of the grandfathers he'd never known: a large fat man with a watch-chain looping from his waistcoat pockets, with a great white beard twice the size of Father Christmas's; who took a roll of thick twist from his pocket and shredded it with a penknife to put in his clay pipe. He saw him like in an old photograph which was growing faint and brown.

He knew Mr Marx had once walked through the streets of Ancoats with his friend, Mr Angel; and as Michael shuffled down Great Ancoats Street, he pretended he was walking with them and showing them things.

'Through that window you can see a man having a bath in a tin bath in front of the fire, and the children have to wait in the yard while the man's wife scrubs him, for he's been digging down the pit. Through that window there's a woman lying on the couch because she's dying of consumption like all women do. And through that window you can see a little baby with bow legs because its got what is called rickets and rhymes with crickets.'

Michael was going to town to sell *Daily Workers*, which he'd got in a canvas bag slung over his shoulders. He stopped at Yates's Wine Lodge, because that was where the Salvation Army sold their papers.

There was still plenty of time when he got to the Wine Lodge, so he studied the window of Fritz the pork butcher next door. Fritz, as always when he wasn't serving, was sharpening his large knife with loud swishes on a large poker; and, as always, was wearing his straw hat and his white and blue striped pinafore. Mrs Fritz, who was very fat and wore a white overall and had yellow hair bobbed at the back, was scrubbing down the wooden chopping-table. When she saw Michael, she beckoned him in. She said something to Fritz, and Fritz handed him half a pork pie.

'Here!' said Fritz. 'You take this. I give it to you. It will not keep fresh until Monday.'

'Ta,' said Michael. 'Ta very much!'

'Ta?' said Mrs Fritz. 'What is that talk? You say "danker shurn".'

'Danker shurn,' said Michael.

'You see,' said Mrs Fritz to Mr Fritz, 'we make him a little German, and all for a piece of pie.'

'You will enjoy the pie,' said Fritz, 'because I am the finest butcher in Manchester.' He then waved Michael away. 'Gooten arbend!'

'Gooten arbend,' said Michael, and he left them to their scrubbing and sharpening. Germans were the nicest people in the whole world. He promised himself he would never kill Germans when he grew up.

Leaning against the wall by the door of the Wine Lodge, he watched the clock on New Cross church. A woman came out of the Wine Lodge with a glass of port wine in her hand. She wore bright red lipstick and her cheeks were rouged in large round circles; her hair had been smoothed to her head with a kiss-curl on her forehead like an upside-down question mark.

'Waiting for your mom and dad, sonny, are you?'

Michael put on his lonely look and said yes.

'Never mind,' she said. 'They'll not be long. Here, have a swig of port, it'll do you good while you're waiting.'

Michael took a sip, but she insisted on him taking a good swallow; she made him drink it all. It was good, and made him belch.

'I'm a totty,' she said. 'Do you know what a totty is?' Michael said he didn't. 'You will some day, chuck,' she said. 'Once you've left school. 'Course I wasn't always a totty. I had a husband once, looked fine in his uniform. Them bloody bitches say he was shot by a firing squad for desertion, and was found in bed with a madamwozel in Nancy. But he wasn't – he was killed on the Somme along with everybody else.'

She gave him a great big long warm wet kiss on his lips; his first ever, for his mam had always pecked him on the forehead. 'There now, chuck,' she said, 'you've been kissed by a totty, but don't tell your mammy.'

She went back inside, and a minute later out came a man with a bowler hat and a shiny watch-chain curving from his waistcoat pockets. 'That tart I'm with says you're waiting for you mam and dad. Happen they'll not be all that long, lad. Here – here's a twopenny cigar for you. Don't let the cops see you smoking it, that's all.'

'Danker shurn,' said Michael.

Michael lit the cigar, and began shouting '*Daily Worker*, one penny!' He saw himself as the hero of Ancoats. He would change the world even if he had to sell a hundred million *Daily Workers* to do it. He saw himself holding a pitchfork in one hand and a red flag in the other, with German pork butchers and Jewish pawn-brokers and even Irish priests looking up at him and smiling because they were happy, and the sun rising behind them. It was something he'd seen on the front of a Communist magazine. Everybody would have bulging wage packets, and eat meat pies and smoke cigars; and there would be train trips to Blackpool each Sunday instead of church; and the sea would be blue, and there would be yachts with white sails, with captains waving merrily to children who were smiling and playing with buckets and spades. Even the donkeys would be smiling, and the railway engines and trams and motor-cars would be smiling like in the comics. In fact, all children would be given a stack of American comics with Orphan Annie every Saturday night, and be allowed to read them in bed until midnight, and Ovaltine would be free. Totties would be given little houses, like in Orphan Annie, where the half-moon shone in a dark blue sky, and the win-dows were lit up yellow; and their houses would be full of silk cushions and ticking clocks, and they'd also be given needlework baskets.

The cigar made him feel a little sick, but he bravely continued shouting, '*Daily Worker*, one penny!' Then a Salvation Army man came along carrying his satchel of papers.

'Scram, sonnie,' growled the man. 'This is God's territory. Go and sell them papers where the Devil lives, not here. Beat it! Go on!'

Michael crossed the road to the *Daily Express* building. He looked down through the windows into the cellars where the machines were rolling out miles and miles of newspaper all joined together; some men in blue overalls were walking around with oilcans; others were reading newspapers which came dropping down already cut and folded from other machines.

And then the knees-up horses came galloping from Jersey Street with their red two-wheeled carts full of bundled news-papers, on their way to the railway stations. It was like a chariot race, and it gave Michael an idea. He stood in front of the building with his *Daily Workers* carefully folded to hide the name, and

shouted, 'All the latest news! Read all about it! One penny!'
People rushed to buy his papers, then rushed away to read them.
He did great business for a few minutes, until a uniformed
commissionaire hurried out and threatened to get him locked up
by the police. What with the Salvation Army man in uniform, and
the commissionaire in uniform, Michael felt threatened. He ran
across New Cross, his only hope now being the market. The
kerosene-crackling, humbug-smelling market. There'd be
thousands of people, and they'd be walking around buying all
sorts of things.

He entered into Tib Street, the animal street where they sold
cocks and hens, rabbits and white mice, pups and kittens. At the
entrance was a man with no legs, who had a fat body on a wooden
platform with tiny iron castors. He used two heavy iron weights to
pull himself along by his hands, clump-clump. He was begging by
means of a gramophone with a large horn. His hand was con-
stantly winding up the gramophone, and he had only one record,
which was 'The Laughing Policeman' and it made everybody
laugh, they couldn't help it; even when they looked down at the
man with no legs they laughed and threw pennies in his cap.
Michael was angry. There shouldn't be any wounded from a war,
and they shouldn't be allowed to be seen. Men should get
themselves killed outright, quickly and cleanly and comfortably,
or not at all. And it was unfair to play laughing gramophone
records. *Ha-ha-ha-ha-ha-ha! Ha-ha-ha-ha-ha-ha!*

A pup-seller was holding two little pups by their necks. The
pups had their eyes closed; they were shivering and dying.
Michael's dad always said they took them from their mothers too
young.

'Last two of the litter!' shouted the pup-seller. 'Shilling each
for a faithful friend!' If they were not sold when the market closed,
they would be dumped in a dustbin, and Michael hoped they
would curl up together amongst the cabbage leaves and die warm
and peaceful.

Ha-ha-ha-ha-ha-ha! Ha-ha-ha-ha-ha-ha!

'Get your fortune told. Find out what fate has in store.'

'Cough mixture for all kinds of coughs.'

'*Daily Worker*, one penny!'

'Humbugs made before your very eyes. Nothing but the best
ingredients, see for yourself.'

'And with every tea service, I'm going to throw in a set of stainless steel cutlery made in Sheffield.'

'Take the little kiddie a toy home! Playful Pluto, little Mickey Mouse's dog!'

'Half the price of what you'll pay in Lewis's.'

'*Daily Worker*, one penny!'

'I'm not asking a pound, I'm not asking ten shillings . . .'

Michael came to the biggest pet shop in Tib Street. In the window was a cage full of pups, lots of lucky little pups because they were in sawdust and had a bowl of water. In the next cage were kittens, and there was a rabbit, and a glass tank full of white mice, and above them on a shelf were bowls of goldfish. But the outside wall upset Michael, for hooked to nails in the bricks were the smallest of boxes with cage fronts, and in the boxes were dozens of wild birds. He knew nothing of wild birds, except that he'd heard names like linnets and finches and thrushes and blackbirds, and he guessed they were those kind of things. All the wild birds were miserable and quiet; the larger birds were in boxes which gave them no room to turn around. Their instinct for life had gone, but Michael didn't know that; he just felt they were homesick and wanted to go back to their families and their trees. A sign said, 'Lovely Little Singers', but even if one of them had decided to sing it wouldn't have been heard, for the calling of the peddlers and the cracking of the carbide flares and the laughing policeman would have stifled its song of the green fields.

'*Ha-ha-ha, ha-ha-ha, ha-ha-ha-ha-ha!*' Michael was forced to laugh as he looked at the wild birds, and he hated himself and the man with the gramophone for he really wanted to cry. On the spur of the moment he rolled a couple of *Daily Workers* up tight, and reaching from his toes turned the wooden latches of the boxes. Most of the cage doors flew open. None of the birds moved.

'Fly off, ye daft little buggers, fly off!' shouted Michael, hitting against the cages to wake them up. 'Get going while the going's good! Ach, ye silly little sods!'

Most of the birds turned their heads away from the freedom he offered them.

A pair of thick hands grabbed him and skuldragged him into the shop and flung him down on a sack of pigeon-corn.

'What the bloody hell d'y'think you're up to, eh? What was that all about?' The man shook him till his teeth rattled.

98

'I don't know, master,' said Michael, frightened.

'Don't know! You must bloody know! You undid all my cages. Why? What's the game?'

'To let the birds free.'

'That's right – to let my birds free. And that's the same as depriving me of stock, and that's the same as stealing.' He called to a woman in a green smock who was weighing out dog biscuits. 'Hilda, fetch the police. We'll see if this little rat can free himself from the cage they're going to put him in.'

'No, please! I don't know why I did it, honest, master.'

'And what's this you're selling? *Daily Workers*? I might have known. Where you from – Ancoats or Collyhurst?'

'Ancoats.'

'Want putting on a ship, towing out to sea, and sinking, you lot. Bleeding no-good immigrants!'

'Yes, sir.'

'Right then, I'll tell you what we'll do. I'll keep all these newspapers, they'll be handy for the bottoms of me birdcages out there; all they're good for anyway.'

'You can't do that, mister. That's stealing too.'

'Best get the police after all, Hilda. It's the only thing these little shits from Ancoats understand.'

Michael dropped his *Daily Workers* and ran out of the shop. He fought his way through the crowds until he got to the other end of Tib Street. There was a man there too, and he was also playing a gramophone, and he had only one leg and only one arm and a lot of medals pinned to his coat, and he was playing what was nearly a laughing song.

'Oh, the penny bazaar, ha-ha-ha-ha! The penny bazaar!'

Michael ate his pork pie under the blanket. The night had started well with the nice Germans and a kiss from the totty which made him lick his lips with the memory, even though they tasted pork-pie. But then the night had turned to terror. And why hadn't those bloody stupid little birds flown away when they'd had the chance? Perhaps nobody could escape anything ever. Perhaps nobody wanted to escape.

Without warning, Liam's house was empty. The curtains were at the window, but there was no jug on the step. There were speculations and excitements that the family might have gassed themselves because there was no money coming in. But somebody laughed and said if there was no money coming in, how the Devil could they afford to put money in the meter to gas themselves? Then somebody else reminded everybody that a family in Harding Street had done that only recently by sawing through the gas-pipe. But Miss Daly had the answer.

'Ah now, they got a letter with their passage money saying their brother was dying in Macroom, and they'd have to go right away. And wouldn't ye think she'd have paid off her tick with the money, instead of gallivinating off to Ireland?'

The lads were very upset by the news, and it was a miserable day for them. It would have been better if Liam's family had gassed themselves, then they wouldn't have been jealous of him. It wasn't fair, and why couldn't they have uncles who were dying, not necessarily in Macroom, but in any part of Ireland, for although they'd been born there none of them really remembered it. When they were younger they pretended they remembered every minute from being new-born babies – that they'd seen the little people in red caps and green jerkins, that they'd heard the banshees howling – but as they grew to boyhood they couldn't tell these lies to each other without looking away. Oh, but Ireland of the weeping people, of the happy weeping people! And there would be Liam with a large golden buckle to his belt, standing among the trees with a silver sword in his hand like a young rapparee, and listening to the diddle-doodle of the tin whistle and the rattling of the fingers on a flat skin drum. And the air would be smelling of early-evening Guinness, and when the owls hooted the Guinnessmen would laugh and sparkle about the olden days of glory.

Only Arthur remained unmoved. He was English and this was England, even though it was only Ancoats. He knew that Ireland was a land of magical bloodshed, and if he ever went there he would be turned into a Catholic immediately.

Kevin and Arthur were not too bothered about Liam's departure, for at the time they were very busy trying to get in the Scouts. Kevin had had to get two references. One was from the girl with the tortoise-shell glasses who looked after the library. She never looked up when signing his reference; but then she never looked up for anything, even when there was a street fight outside, or when the horse dropped dead, or when the airship flew over the town – not even when MacSweeney's pipers marched down Every Street on Saint Patrick's Day. The other reference was from Miss Hindshaw at the museum. When Kevin called, she was in a good mood and would have signed anything; she told him that an old tramp had sold her a valuable book for half a crown. It was *The Manchester Man* and was a first edition of 1876; priceless, she said it was.

The 102nd Troop met in a wooden hut at the side of the Roundhouse. There were two patrols, the owl and the beaver; but the owl patrol, the one they were put in, was the best because in a wooden cupboard on their side of the wall was a stuffed owl which Mr Harvey, the scoutmaster, had bought with troop funds from the local pawnbroker. The beaver patrol always hoped that someday they would get a stuffed beaver, but Mr Harvey explained that beavers were difficult to obtain in Ancoats, or anywhere else in Britain.

Kevin had had to discuss the matter of joining a Scout troop with his dad, previously. His father had been a bit worried about the Scouts and the Roundhouse, particularly when he'd been told that Mr Harvey was the manager of Williams the Deacons Bank.

'Sure there's something in the name of Williams and him being a deacon that isn't right, and I'd be hating to be thinking that the penny a week subscription I give you ends up in a Protestant bank,' he'd said. But worse was the news about the oath.

'I have to hold the Union Jack in my left hand, and do the Scout salute with my right, and take the oath.'

'And what'd that oath be, if I may be so bold?'

'I promise on my honour to do my best to do my duty to God and the King; to help other people at all times, and to obey the Scout laws.'

'I see now,' said his dad, twirling his pointed moustache, even though there was no soap on it, for normally he soaped his moustache before twirling it into a needle. There was such a silence you could hear the man and woman fighting in the house two doors away.

'Now I don't mind you learning them German songs,' said his dad, at last, 'for the Germans is very fine people, and I've had to kill many a good one of 'em during the war. But it's not all that many years ago since there was the most wicked and deadly slaughter between Irishman and Irishman over the taking of the oath of allegiance, and that's a different matter altogether.'

'I know, dad.'

His father twirled his moustache again. 'Well now, I can see you like the dressing up for the Boy Scouts and doing the knots and them other things, and 'tis a good thing for you to do, even though it's at the Settlement. So I'll be encouraging you to stay with them. And you may hold the flag and take the oath of allegiance, but – and here's a big "but" now, my son –' he prodded the boy with his finger – 'You mustn't mean it. D'y'hear that, now? You can say it, but not mean it. And I'm thinking that's a reasonable compromise.' His dad looked mighty pleased with himself at his own wisdom, and Kevin hugged him, then hugged his mam, and said a Scout was always supposed to honour his mother and father.

He and Arthur were as proud as Boggart Hole Clough peacocks as they strutted to the Settlement on the swearing-in night. Kevin held the flag and stared at the stuffed owl which had been brought out of its cupboard for the occasion. It was the owl he was going to say his words to, and not the flag. When he came to mention the King, he thought to himself, 'Dear Jesus, I don't mean it.' Mr Harvey shook hands with him and gave him the tassels for his shirt and the badge for his jacket. And then it was Arthur's turn; but Arthur wanted to go home because he was always tongue-tied in front of an audience and he just couldn't get his words out.

'I promise,' said Arthur, and was unable to say any more.

'Help him, Kevin,' said Mr Harvey, and Kevin knew he had to help him for a Scout was a friend to all and a brother to every other Scout. He gripped Arthur's hand on the flag.

'On my honour,' said Kevin.

'On my honour,' repeated Arthur; and that's how it went on until it got to the King. But Kevin worked it out that Arthur was a Saxon, so he would have to mean it for Arthur because the King of England was Arthur's King.

'To God and the King,' said Kevin, and he thought, 'Dear Jesus, what I am saying I mean for Arthur but, if you remember, I don't mean it for me.'

The first thing he did when they left the Scout Hut was to thump Arthur's shoulder to emphasize what he was going to say.

'So if the King tells you to do summat, you've got to do it. But if he tries to boss me around I can say, "Not today, thank you".'

Arthur didn't quite understand, so he wiped his nose on his sleeve and snorted.

They skipped down the entry into Dunn Street, and there leaning against the wall were Patrick, Sean and Michael. They did nothing and said nothing, but stared wistfully at Liam's door; at the door of the boy who had gone to Ireland, to the land known only in song. Kevin joined them without question; he too put his hands in his pocket and gazed at the door.

It was a dark brown door with a number nine hanging almost upside down from one screw, so that it nearly made a number six. At the bottom were upside-down mountain-peak stains where Liam's dad had spilled beer from his jug on the occasions it had rained suddenly when he'd been swigging it on the step. There were four panels in the door, also of dark brown wood except for one panel which had been repaired after Liam's father had once put his fist through it. It had been filled with plywood from a packing case and then painted over, but the paint showed the words 'Ceylon Tea' through it. The doorknob was brass, but it had once been painted white which had partly worn away, leaving the knob like a little world with a grey continent on a golden sea. There was netting with large holes in it at the window, and behind it stood a statue of the Virgin Mary which gave Liam's mother a lot of trouble, for she never knew which was the orthodox way to turn the Mother of God. Mostly she turned her inwards to face the room, except when they were having a bath in front of the fire. Mary was also turned to face the street when Liam's mother went out foraging for food. The blind was down at the upstairs window. But it was the door which took up the boys silent attention, for the door was Ireland to them. Except, of course, for Arthur, who, with one foot on the pavement and the other on the cobbles, hopped and strode over the gutter in search of treasure.

The time went by, and there was no sign of the return of the boy from Ireland. Each night they leaned on the wall and stared at the door; sometimes they had a fight; sometimes they didn't. And then Sean broke the news that the milk jug had been on the step that morning and the Virgin Mary was looking inward again.

They watched and waited for Liam to come out, but come out he did not; although once or twice they thought they saw the upstairs curtain move. He wasn't at school either. So what the Devil was going on?

After some days they saw him running back from Miss Daly's with a loaf of bread, and they nabbed him, and they frogmarched him on to the croft for him to tell them about Ireland.

''Tis the finest country in the world,' he said. 'And the things I've seen! And the things I've done! Sure I shouldn't be wasting me time with the likes of you lot!'

They bribed him with bits and pieces from their pockets.

'I've sailed a boat on one of the lakes of Killarney,' he said.

'How big was it?'

'Twelve inches.'

'Not the boat, the lake?'

'Oh, very big. It stretched to the other side.'

'Of what?'

'Of the lake. Then I kissed the Blarney Stone.'

'What's that?'

'A big stone upside down on the top of a ruined castle.'

'What did ye kiss a stone for? Was there no girls?'

'It makes you talk. It gives you the gift of elegance.'

'It's not done you much good,' said Kevin, contemptuously, 'if all you can say about the lake of Killarney is that it stretches to the other side.'

'Best was,' said Liam, 'when I went on horseback, which made me bum sore, across the wicked mountains of County Cork to a little white house where they opened a trunk and let me hold the uniform as was worn by Michael Collins himself, and let me put the cap on me head as was worn by Michael Collins, the hero of Ireland.'

'Who's Michael Collins?'

'Ach, ye're an ignorant bunch o' flamers, that ye are, and not knowing a blooming thing about the land what has given ye birth. If ye don't know who he was, then I'm not telling you, and that's that.'

'Did you see the little people?' asked Terence.

'And am I not talking this very minute to them, for sure you're the littlest people I've ever known,' said Liam, and he lifted his leg up high and broke wind. 'Catch that!' he shouted. Then he suddenly looked unhappy; he lowered his leg slowly and felt his trousers. 'Aw, Jesus, I've messed meself!'

'That comes of kissing the Blarney Stone,' said Kevin.

A week later there was depressing news for the gang. Liam and his mam and dad were going back to Ireland for keeps. The dead uncle had left them his cottage. It had never been known for a family to go back to Ireland, and many people in the neighbourhood went out of their way to pass the house in Dunn Street from which the people inside were going to return to Erin's green isle.

'It's not fair,' said Patrick; 'nobody should be allowed to leave Ancoats and us having to stay here. Some day there'll be kids blacking O'Rourke's horses for you and me.'

'It's the biggest farm in all Ireland,' Liam told the gang. 'And with a thousand cows, five hundred pigs, ten thousand geese and over a hundred champion racehorses.'

His father's description in the Spread Eagle differed from his son's. ''Tis but a few acres for the peat and the spuds, and the cottage is wanting a roof. But 'tis better than going in the workhouse.'

Nobody believed it at first; not until Liam's mother raffled the Virgin Mary, and then everybody knew it was for certain.

Liam wanted to spend his last day with the gang playing on the Crimean cannon in Philips Park. This huge ugly cannon had been cemented into the ground for the children to play on. It pointed to the faraway hills which were the Pennines, and on the other side of which was said to be Yorkshire. It was so stuffed with rubbish that, if it could ever have been fired, the whole of Yorkshire would have been covered in toffee papers as if it were snowing.

The game was for as many kids as possible to sit astride the long muzzle, right to the open mouth of the cannon; then they tried to push each other off. Almost every week there was a broken shoulder or a broken arm or a badly bruised head; the cannon caused more casualties among the kids of Ancoats than ever it had done in the Crimea.

In the evening, all the lads stayed in their houses and sniffed with sadness. None of them could bear to see Liam's family walking to the station to catch the midnight train to Holyhead.

Night came, and Arthur had to do his duty, which was to sit on the lavatory in the yard and sing a Protestant hymn. This ritual had been arranged by the gang. None of them was allowed to take a candle out to the lavatory except at Christmas when people called; well, it was a waste of a good candle, for a boy could do what he wanted to do without having to look to see what he'd done. The trouble was that most of the boys liked a cigarette before going to bed, and none of their parents allowed them to carry matches in their pockets. Arthur was lucky – his mother didn't mind him taking a candle out; so Arthur sat on the lavatory seat with his trousers around his ankles, for even though he didn't want to do anything it didn't seem right sitting on a lavatory without first taking his trousers down. Then he sang his hymn to let the lads know he was on duty, and they could sneak out of their backyards and into his lavatory to get a light from his candle.

Jesus bids us shine with a pure clear light,
Like a little candle burning in the night.

One by one the boys would tiptoe in, light their Woodbine, and creep away again. Not knowing what the singing was all about, there were some neighbours who commented that the lad could become a religious maniac if not watched closely.

In this world of darkness we must shine,
You in your small corner and I in mine.

The last lad to turn up that night was Liam. It was to be his last cigarette before starting off for the train. Arthur noticed that Liam was crying.

'Been peeling onions, have you?'

'I don't want to go, Arthur,' Liam said. 'I want to stay. They'll make me a priest, that's what they'll do. All me Aunties say what a good priest I'll make, and me uncles say it, and me mam and dad say it, and even the priest in Macroom said it, and he speaks the old language which is harder than doing sums. And I don't want to be a priest. I want to stay in Ancoats and be a gunman.'

Sean and Terence found a dog; well, they didn't exactly find it, they stole it; no, that's not true, they rescued it. It was the day the two of them kicked cans and swung from lamp posts all the millions of miles to Platt Fields. There had been a Punch and Judy show in one of the fields, but it had finished until the next performance. The man lay in the grass at the back of the booth and poured himself out a tin mug of beer. His dog, Dog Toby, begged to him, and he poured some beer out in a tin plate for the dog, which it lapped up as though it had never had a drink in its life. And then, for no apparent reason, the man lost his temper with the dog. He kicked it, and it yelped. He threw his beer mug at it, and it yelped again, and ran across the field towards Sean and Terence.

'You're the worst Dog Toby I've ever had,' shouted the man. 'You beg for beer when you should be begging the crowds for money!'

The lads snatched the dog, and cleared off home with it as fast as their legs would carry them. Sean loved dogs; he still prayed for the soul of his poor drowned Tiny. He was desperate for a dog to love; but his father clamped down on the idea of him keeping this new dog at home. Had he not been hauled over the coals by Constable Donovan for dumping the last dog in the cut after it had been destroyed? He wasn't going to have that happen all over again. However, Mr Taffy said he could keep it in the stable with Dobbin; which was just as well, for all the people in Sean's street had to leave home for the night, by order of the Town Hall, and all animals had to be turned out in the street because they couldn't be taken where the people were being sent.

The Town Hall decreed that all the houses in the street were to be sealed up and gassed because of the bugs. With the weather getting nicer, the bugs had become worse. They crawled over the wallpaper in full view; they sometimes dropped into the food and had to be spooned out; they bit people in their beds and made it painful to try and sleep; indeed, some people wrapped themselves up and sat out on the steps all night when it was warm. The families were taken in open trucks on the 8th Ardwick Battalion barracks. They weren't allowed to take any belongings, and they had to be covered in powder, and they had to sleep on the wooden floor. Most of them were more afraid of being in an English barracks guarded by English soldiers than they were of the bugs.

Sean watched the houses being gassed. Men sealed up the fireplaces and windows with brown paper and sticky tape; then they set fire to some tins of powder, which hissed and hissed; then they ran out and slammed the doors, and covered the doors with sheets of rubber.

When the families returned they felt important because

neighbours asked them what it was like, it being their turn next, or next after that. But the awful smell of the gas stayed behind; it lingered for ever, and sometimes people spewed up with it. Although some of the nights were cold, they had to sleep with the windows wide open. When a cupboard was opened, there was a whiff of the gas. When they got in bed under the blankets, coats and rugs, the stink of the gas was thick and heavy. Even teapots and kettles were filled with the stink of fumigation; some said you could pour the stink out from the spouts; some said they'd rather have lived with the bugs.

Sean couldn't wait to get back to his dog in the stable. He had decided to call him just plain Toby, because, after all, Toby would know he was a dog, and everybody could see he was a dog, so why bother saying 'Dog'?

Toby seemed listless and unhappy and Sean began petting him. He hardly noticed Mrs Taffy coming in to the stable. She was smiling at him.

'Come here,' said Mrs Taffy. She beckoned him to her, and something made him go. She put an arm around his shoulders and held him to her. She put her other hand down his trousers and played with him.

'What have I found?' she asked. 'Ah, a little cake with a cherry on top.'

The sensation to Sean was new and divine. He was warm and he tingled. He felt he no longer had a body, but had become an angel suspended in mid-air. Then she took her hand away. 'You're too young, aren't you?' she said. 'Never mind; you'll get the surprise of your life one of these fine days.' She walked out of the stable and, although still smiling, became Mrs Taffy again. 'I've got a bowl you can have for the dog,' she said.

Sean left the stable whistling 'Once In Royal David's City'. It was nowhere near Christmas, but there was a crib in his imagination which held a gentle magical lady and an innocent naked baby, king of the universe, with animals looking on. He knew he could never tell his pals about his experience. He knew he certainly could not mention it to Mr Taffy.

Mr Beaumont had chalked a composition title on the blackboard. It was 'How I spent Saturday'. He told them he'd be back in half an hour, and woe betide anybody who hadn't worked. As soon as he left the classroom, there was the usual flirting of ink pellets from rulers, and the usual slamming down of desktops, and the occasional breaking of wind in a loud manner which would get a response of 'Come on in and wipe your feet'. After that, they all settled down to rapid dipping of ink and scratching of pens.

In less than a minute Arthur put his pen down and folded his arms to show that he'd finished. The others had barely begun. Kevin couldn't resist looking at Arthur's exercise book, and it read: 'I got up, and I read comics all day, and I went to bed.'

'That's not enough,' Kevin said.

'But it's all I did,' said Arthur.

'He'll want more than that. You'll get the strap.'

'But it's all I –'

'Listen, make it up. That's what I'm doing. Say you saw a lion at Belle Vue, or went for coke to the gasworks, or played on the Crimean cannon or something. Make it interesting.'

Arthur wiped his nose on his sleeve, and picked up his pen again with a sigh.

Mr Beaumont came back. 'Well, now, let's see what you've been up to. I heard a loud noise of writing as I was coming up the corridor.' He pointed to Betty. 'Betty, please!'

'I got up very early and brownstoned de step for my movver and cleaned de windows, den I went errands for my movver, den I helped my movver do de ironing. Den der was a little mouse in de trap and it was not dead because it had not catched its neck but catched its legs and I put it down de lavatory. Den I peeled de potatoes for my movver, and swilled de backyard for my movver, and washed de pots for my movver. At night my movver took me to de pictures which was about cowboys.'

'Very factual, if nothing else,' said Mr Beaumont. 'Arthur, what bright little gem of literature have you got for us?'

'I climbed to the top of the big gasometer and I jumped off and a man caught me and said what was I doing and I said I was looking for a lion and he said he had seen a lion eating a tramp outside the tramp ward and I pulled its tail and it surrendered and a keeper came and took it back to Belle Vue.'

'A very frightening day for you,' said Mr Beaumont. 'Now, Kevin! We're all breathless with anticipation.'

Kevin looked around to make sure everybody was paying

attention before he began: 'I walked out and Ancoats was gone. The sun was no longer a red ball because of the smoke, but was too dazzling to look at. An invisible street organ was playing 'Rosie O'Grady' and it sounded hollow and came from the sky. Everywhere was thick green with grass, and coloured birds was flying. And there was fish swimming in the river. Then at night the stars was shining because the mills was not working, and the stars made a noise like the railway wagons shunting, and the moon screamed like it was a girl being murdered. Then the smoke came and all went black and it was Ancoats again. So I went to sleep.'

'If I'd asked for fantasy and imagination, I might have given you ten out of ten for that little composition. But I asked what you *did*, on Saturday, not what you thought.'

'Yes, sir.'

The bell rang for home time. Kevin and Arthur rushed out into the street. Sean was waiting for them; he had Toby on a piece of string.

'I think Toby is going to die, and I'm not going to let him be drowned,' he said, with tears coming from his eyes. 'And I thought you'd come with me to the Spread Eagle to see Mr Tipperary Tim, being as he's a friend of your dad's and being as Mr Tipperary Tim is as good as a doctor, as everyone knows.'

'What's up with Toby?' asked Kevin.

'He won't eat and he won't drink, and he'll starve to death.'

'I'll show you who Mr Tipperary Tim is,' said Kevin. 'But don't let him take Toby for dog oil.'

'That's another reason for me wanting you to come with me; for you're fast with the knife and you won't let him take Toby for oil.'

Tipperary Tim, him with the blue tattoos of bare women and ships on his arms, worked with Kevin's dad. He shovelled the rubbish into the roaring blazing boilers, and he had one boiler set aside for dead dogs which were found in the middens and given to him for a penny each by the Dolly Varden men when they came in with their horses and carts.

Once or twice a day he would scoop up the oil from the cremated dogs and pour it into bottles which also came from the middens but were well-washed by steam from the boilers. He sold his bottles of dog oil for twopence a bottle; and dog oil was the finest cure that ever there was for cuts and scratches, applied outwardly, or diseases and illnesses of all natures, taken inwardly.

Dog oil was wonderful for scarlet fever, whooping cough, croup and meningitis, and all the other diseases that came up from the drains and took away one child in every five. And, of course, at twopence a bottle it was much cheaper than paying a doctor's bill.

'Sure them people in the countryside where the grass is green has their own natural cures which they call the herbs,' Mr Tipperary Tim would explain. 'But in the towns where there's only the black bricks growing, our natural cures is called dead dogs, for did ye ever see a dog with meningitis?'

Kevin promised he wouldn't let Mr Tipperary Tim take Toby away for dog oil. On their way to the Spread Eagle, Kevin had to call in at the library. Mr Beaumont had given him a list of books to give to the girl with the tortoise-shell glasses; and he had to read all those books as punishment.

'All at the same time?' asked Sean.

'No, ye daft sod, one at a time! It's to punish me for being a mick and a Catholic. And it's to make me eyes go blind, and with me not even being able to play the fiddle. Mr Beaumont is a big Saxon shit!'

'Then don't read 'em.'

'Oh aye, and get the strap in front of Betty and snotty-nosed Arthur here? Ah no, I'll read them bloody books, and I'll get revenge on Mr Beaumont.'

'How?'

'By enjoying them. But he'll never know.' He thumped Arthur. 'And if you ever tell him, I'll kill you.'

'He punishes me worse than he punishes you,' said Arthur. 'For he throws chalk at me forehead, and me mam says me skin will get hard and I'll grow a horn like a rhinoceros.'

Sean carried Toby in his arms to the Spread Eagle. He was sad, and to make him even sadder, Blind Andy was playing 'I'll Take You Home Again, Kathleen'. He dropped a ha'penny in the fiddler's cap.

'I'm only giving ye a ha'penny, Mr Blind Andy,' said he, 'for I don't like the tune you're playing.'

'It's an Irish tune.'

'I don't care.'

'Ah, now isn't that it, then?' sighed Andy. 'Ireland is nothing else but a melody that nobody wants. If every Irishman in the world, or every man who thinks he's Irish, or every man who wants to be Irish, would only contribute one ha'penny a week to the land he sings about, sure Ireland would be the richest country in the world. I thank you, and God bless you!'

As soon as the lads reached the step of the beerhouse, Toby wriggled out of Sean's arms before he could stop him, and tottered over the sawdust on the floor.

'Well, now,' said Michael's dad. ''Tis a drop o'beer this animal will be wanting.' And he held his pot for Toby to lap, which Toby did. 'Ah, will ye look at that, now! And don't I know how he feels?'

Kevin's dad offered Toby a piece of pork pie, and Toby ate it. 'The poor little bugger,' said Kevin's dad.

Sean stood in the doorway and watched. Everybody in the pub began watching. It was a miracle. Toby's stump of a tail wagged like a fan, and after a few more laps of beer he stood up on its hind legs, then dropped on his bottom to sit up and beg for more pork pie. And all the men showed their appreciation in the usual manner by clapping their hands.

'What's his name?' asked Mr Kelly.

'Toby.'

'Would ye believe that, then, eh? Toby. Toby Jug, that's what it is – Tobyjug.'

Mr Kelly said he'd like to keep Tobyjug to give him a good home, and there'd always be food and drink, and there'd always be good company to do his tricks for, and he would be the happiest dog in the whole of the great city of Manchester and beyond.

At first, Sean said no. He called Toby, but Toby was too busy showing off.

'And ye can come any time ye like, as long as ye come in through the backyard door. And here you'll find Tobyjug curled up on the hearth rug in front o' the fire and dreaming of opening time; sure 'tis the life o' Riley he'll be leading. Come on now, give Tobyjug his freedom, eh? What d'y'say?'

Sean kissed Toby and joined the other two. He and Arthur sat on the library steps while Kevin went in to see if his list was ready, Sean still weepy about the parting. 'Not only have I lost me fine wonderful dog,' he told Arthur, 'but I've lost me excuse for going up to the stable in the evening when Mr Taffy is asleep and snoring on the couch, and him being miles away and not aware of anything.'

Chemical breezes of summer

The sky over the mill tops outside the classroom was the grey of a midden-tin lid. The sun was a red ball in the sky because of the smoke from the rubber works, chemical breezes with sweet smells wafted along the corridors. The lamplighter didn't light the lamps until after ten o'clock at night. And most children knew by these signs that it was the season called summer.

It was Friday afternoon reading time and the book was *Hereward The Wake*. Mr Beaumont had left them to it, but the classroom door was wide open so that any outbreak of loud noise in the class would be heard and dealt with in a rush. Some of the boys made scales out of rulers and balanced the small white pot inkwells on them; some broke the points of nibs to make darts; some held glass alleys to the light to examine the red, blue, orange and green whirls inside the glass. The girls were pretending to read, but were in fact giggling and whispering. There was singing coming from the hall:

Where are you going to, my pretty maid?
Where are you going, my honey?
Over the hill, kind sir, she said,
To my father a-mowing the barley.

Kevin tried to make his mind a complete blank by staring at a picture called 'Wind in a Cornfield'. Arthur, next to him, had trapped a fly in his desk, and every few seconds lifted the lid about half an inch to peep in and see if he could see the fly. Betty, behind them, was using two fingers to be little dancing figures, and they were doing the can-can on the desk top which was a stage before the Queen.

Kevin came out of his yellow haze. He watched Arthur peeping under the lid, then he slowly and quietly took the inkwell out of its hole in Arthur's desk. This should have allowed the fly to escape and thereby make a fool of Arthur, but no fly bothered to escape.

It was a school fly, and no doubt had long since decided it was safer to go along with the games the kids played, otherwise there might be a sudden end to all existence from an exercise book. It was probably in a dark corner waiting for Arthur's occasional eye.

Kevin sighed with boredom and turned round to Betty. She was whispering, 'Dance little lady, dance a-pie', to her dancing fingers. He smacked the palm of his hand down on her fingers. She put them in her mouth and sucked them and kicked her feet about to show she was in pain. Kevin then pushed Arthur's desk lid down, and it caught Arthur's nose; he held it, and he too kicked his feet about to show he was in pain.

'I'm fed up,' said Kevin. 'Me best friend is a Saxon bastard, and me sweetheart – her behind – is an Ulster Protestant. 'Tis not at all how it should be. And there's me with a note to go to the clinic for glasses because me teacher is making me blind.'

'You'll look nice in glasses,' said Betty.

'Why don't you wash your face? You've always got a dirty face. I think you clean the floor with it when you're helping your mother. I'm talking to snotty-nose.'

'You just said I'm your sweetheart.'

'Aye, and if ye bloody tell anybody I'll ram me two fists in your eyes, and ye'll be squinting for the rest of your life.'

'I wish I could have glasses,' said Arthur. ''Cos then if I was given sums to do, I could accidentally break them on purpose and say I couldn't see to do me sums.'

'Suppose Tarzan was to be wearing glasses?' said Kevin. 'Sure them chimpanzees would laugh at him, and wouldn't the elephants turn their big bums to him?'

'He's on his way down the corridor!' shouted one of the lads who was keeping watch. Everybody glanced down quickly at their books.

'Quick! What's a Wake?' whispered Arthur.

'Ah,' said Kevin. 'That's summat ye'll not be knowing, for it's when there's a funeral, and there's everybody drinking the whisky and stout, and tea for them as wants it, and there's the shouting of what a fine one was the one in the coffin, and there's the singing of the old songs, and there's the eating of boiled ham.'

Mr Beaumont entered his classroom, back-kicked the door closed, smiled, and rubbed his hands together.

'Well now, I'm sure we've all been very industrious, haven't we?

Let me see. Hereward the Wake. Arthur, tell us all about Hereward the Wake.'

'Please, sir, he went to a lot of funerals.'

'I see,' said Mr Beaumont, and a corner of his mouth twitched. 'Anything else?'

'Yes, sir. He ate a lot of boiled ham.'

'And did you get all that precious information from the book?'

'No, sir.'

'Where, then, if I may ask.'

Kevin, afraid that Arthur might blab on him, kicked his shin. Arthur hopped away from the desk, rubbing his ankle.

'I made it up, sir. And it wasn't nothing what Kevin said,' he gasped.

'There's no need for you to hop around like a cocksparrow. Sit down. Unless of course you're demonstrating some sort of a dance which Hereward the Wake did at funerals after he'd eaten the boiled ham.' Mr Beaumont flung a piece of chalk which hit Kevin right square in the middle of his forehead. 'Kevin, see me after the bell.'

Kevin rubbed his eyes so that all the class would witness he was going blind. Another bloody book, he thought.

The book he was set as punishment for giving false information was *Three Men in a Boat*, and he told Arthur and Betty, who were waiting for him at the gate, that he intended, just for spite, to enjoy every page of it as if each word was a piece of banana split; he might, for further revenge on Mr Beaumont, even read some of the books his dad brought home for the fire.

'I think you're very brave,' said Betty.

'Sure that's a fact,' said Kevin. 'And 'twas riding the dragon as did it.'

'When are you going to take me to see a tree?'

'In a couple of weeks. But you'll have to wash your face, for haven't ye the muckiest face I've ever seen?'

The following Monday, Betty wasn't at school; there was a note to say she was poorly. Kevin called around at the house, but her dad said it was best if he stopped calling for a wee while, just a wee while. He wrote her little notes saying what had been done in class, and shoved them under her door. At one point he considered leaving a bottle of dog oil on the step, but he changed his mind because he didn't really believe in dog oil.

Arthur tried to be funny about it. 'Dog oil might cure your measles,' he giggled. 'But it could give you pups.' Kevin thumped him for saying daft things, and Arthur got him some fresh flowers from the cemetery, which Kevin left on the step in a jam jar. He also made up his mind to give her a tree, which he knew would please her and probably make her better. He got a saucepan, which had lost its handle and had been doing nothing in a middentin. He managed to scrape enough dirt from under the bricks on the croft, and he planted an orange pip. When he left it on the step, he also left a note to say if she watered it every day it would grow into a tree, and she would have oranges whenever she wanted them, and he had chosen an orange tree because her dad was an Orangeman and looked very smart in his bowler hat, white gloves and silk sash. He hoped she would be better by Saturday, for that was the day he intended taking her to Platt Fields. He'd saved up enough money for the tram fare, and even enough to go on the rowing boats on the lake. But on Friday Mr Beaumont called the register, and then in a soft voice told the class that Betty had died.

That Betty had died! The sound came in circles of *yow-yow-yow* to Kevin's ears; his toes tingled; he couldn't feel the pen he was holding. He suddenly felt very holy and very special. All Ancoats would look at him, and they'd tell each other that he was the boy whose sweetheart had died. But his mind became perplexed, and he was compelled to talk about it that night when the gang had gathered.

It was a warm night. It was after ten o'clock and the lamps had been lit, but people were sitting out on their steps, the men with jugs of beer and the women with mugs of tea. Nobody bothered to send their kids to bed; it was, indeed, much too warm.

As usual, the boys had cigarettes but no matches, and Patrick climbed up a lamp post, opened the glass and lit his cigarette from the gas-mantle. He tossed his cigarette down for the others to get a light, then continued swinging from the arm of the lamp post.

'Suppose she's gone to heaven,' said Kevin, 'and suppose I live to be a hundred. Then when I finally drop dead and meet up with her, I'll be like her great-great-grandfather. And all I'll be able to do is tell her what I did when I was alive. And it won't be the same, will it? It won't be like doing the same things at the same age.'

116

'Perhaps they go to school and start work in heaven,' said Terence. 'Then you'll both be the same age.'

'Ah, but don't ye see, she'll be better educated than what I am, for they must have better schools up there, for they know everything that can be known, and she might become all snobby.'

'They don't work in heaven,' said Michael. 'Not since Karl Marx got there. Everything's found.'

'Like in the workhouse,' said Sean.

'Sure that's right,' added Patrick, dropping down from the lamp post. 'You help yourself to anything what's going, as long as you thank God for putting it your way.'

'Worst is,' said Kevin, 'she's a Protestant and I'm a Catholic. She mightn't be allowed in heaven.'

'You're only half a Catholic,' said Arthur, 'for you go to my school and that makes you half a Protestant.'

'I'm a full Catholic on Sunday. And suppose I die on a Sunday when God's called me name on the register?'

'You'll see her in purgatory, in that case,' said Terence.

'But we don't have purgatory,' said Arthur.

'Ah, 'twill be hell for the pair of ye,' said Sean. 'And maybe your punishment will be you being old enough to be her great-great-grandad.'

'I'd ask to be transferred.'

'Ach, ye blooming galoot, 'tis not like going from one school to another. Anybody what tries to transfer from hell up to heaven is a blooming heretic.'

'Anything's possible with God,' argued Kevin. 'If he's a mind to it.'

'Hey, shut up! Let's all shut up!' whispered Terence. ''Tis blasphemy we're blathering.'

'He can't see us. It's gone dark.'

'Aye, but he can hear us. I'm thinking we should be calling each other by different names when we're running God down. Like I say, "Hello, Billy, and what d'y'think about God Almighty?" And you say, "Hello, Charlie, God gets drunk on a Saturday night and invents a giraffe."'

''Tis a splendid notion,' said Michael. 'And with names like them, he'd think we was English kids, and England would lose the next war.'

Kevin blew out the candle that night with certain problems over

117

Betty's future resolved. She could no longer be his sweetheart, but she could be his sister, his never-born sister. And she could hover above him and look down upon him and watch everything he did, even when he was on the lavatory. She would wait for him. Then when he died, he would arrange for her to see some trees; that's if they bothered with trees up there.

Next morning he looked up her street to make sure the coffin wasn't in the street, for sometimes, if there was overcrowding in the house, the coffin had to be kept on trestles outside the window, where it was lit up at night with works-diggings lamps in case a drunk fell over it. If it had been there, he would have stayed guard with his knife all night, although there had never been any case of anybody stealing a body in a coffin. He was satisfied she was in the parlour.

A few days later, the school bell rang in the middle of afternoon lessons. Mr Beaumont called for the class to stand up and keep quiet. The chanting and singing in the other classrooms stopped abruptly. Outside was the *clip-clop-clippety-clop* of the funeral horse. What a famous thing this was for Betty, Kevin thought; this little girl who had never seen a tree, who had never travelled beyond Pin Mill Brow and Arwick Green, which wasn't green at all, to have the whole school stand up as she passed! There followed the *cloppety-clop-clop* of the parents' carriage, and he knew her mam and dad would be crying. The sound of iron on the cobbles died away. The bell rang, and the sound of learning began again.

'How do you say dip-what's-its-name?' whispered Arthur.

'Dip – theria,' Kevin whispered back.

'I'll bet Betty said "differia" when they told her.'

Suddenly, Kevin's eyes misted, and he wanted to kick himself because a stupid uncontrollable teardrop ran down his face.

'Kevin,' snapped Mr Beaumont, 'I've forgotten to post a letter. I want you to take it to the nearest pillarbox in Great Ancoats Street right away. It's a long way, so I'll not expect you back.'

What a galoot Mr Beaumont is, thought Kevin as he left the school; doesn't he know there's a pillar-box just outside the school? His mind was full of Betty. He guessed exactly where the hearse would be: climbing through Holt Town towards the gasworks on its way to Philips Park cemetery. He was bothered about her not being a Catholic, and instinct took him to Saint

118

Anne's. He would have gone inside the church but he was afraid of Father Sullivan, so instead he stood outside the school and listened. Like Every Street, it was a singing school, but it sang about Jesus whereas his new school sang about buttercups.

Sweet Sacrament of Peace, here in my aching heart,
Where restless yearnings cease, and sorrows all depart.

That was the hymn one window was singing, but the song in Kevin's mind superimposed itself over the hymn.

Where are you going to, my pretty maid?
Where are you going, my honey?
Over the hill, kind sir, she said,
To my father a-mowing the barley.

He was in a fog of sissie tears. He ran across Every Street in front of a tram which ding-dinged and flashed its one front eye. He ran down into Palmerston Street and climbed through a gap in the heavy upright railway sleepers guarding the river, and flung himself down on the mud of the bank. There was noise from the Providence Iron Foundry at the side of the river, '*Shoom-shoom-gurr-snap-balung!*', loud enough to cover the sound of his sobs. The monster sparks and the red glows from the foundry reflected in the Medlock and in the wet face of a huddled, skriking kid.

There was a day in summer when all Ancoats went to Daisy Nook; though for the life of them, nobody knew why. It was tradition, and families never mixed on that day; they walked behind each other up Ashton Old Road. If a man stopped to tie his bootlace, every man behind stopped to tie his bootlace too, in order that they would not have to mix. And all they did was walk up a dreary canal, surrounded by mills which got larger and larger, then stop in a sooty field and watch an ox being roasted. They all said the same thing; 'Sure, we can't afford one of them ox sandwiches.' And they all walked back to Ancoats again.

Patrick for one was glad to cross the Medlock and get back to his home territory; it was a treat for him to get his hands dirty again by gliding them along the walls, and his knee bruised by tripping over a broken upturned grid, and his nose blackened by wiping it with his hands.

For some reason, Terence hadn't been on the Daisy Nook pilgrimage, and when Patrick met him he was studying Miss Daly's window with a pencil and notebook in his hand. He explained he was doing a competition which the wireless had told him to do. His mother had recently bought a wireless; it was the first and only wireless set in Ancoats, and Father Sullivan had made some comment upon it from the pulpit. Was it not a heathenish contraption which made sound waves go through the walls of houses, carrying with them the sounds of Protestant hymns?

'What you doing?

'There's this feller by the name of Romany,' Terence explained. 'And he has a dog called Raq and he lives in a caravan like a tinker. It's all invisible, for everything the wireless says is invisible. And he spends his time looking for little animals. "Ah," says he, "just look at that funny squirrel running up a tree to hide nuts," says he.'

'What does he say "look" for, if ye can't see?'

'You've got to imagine. And then he says, "Look, there's a mole and it's going down a grid."'

'Has he seen an ox?'

'Last week he nearly saw an ox, but it was hidden by a tree.'

'What is an ox?'

''Tis biblical. 'Tis summat ye don't covet.'

'What's "covet"?'

'Aw, piss off. I've got me competition to do.'

'What's the competition?'

'He said we'd to take a stroll outside the house and write down all the birds and beasts we saw. There,' said Terence, pointing in the window, 'is a robin on them Robin's Starch packets. And there's a parrot on that Sharp's toffee tin. And there's a zebra on that blacklead packet. And there's lions on them golden syrup tins. And there's a big fish on that John West tin which has been in her window so long that it must have been caught by Mr Noah. Down, Raq! Good dog!'

He stroked an invisible dog as he jotted names down. Patrick stared at him, and almost looked for the dog. 'Father Sullivan was right,' said Patrick, 'for the wireless set will send you off your rocker. And ye can't send that blooming list in to the Roman. Lions and zebras and parrots! Sure he'll wonder what kind of a place Ancoats is with them things roaming round. And what'll ye sign it? Trader Horn?'

'I'll order Raq to kill in a minute,' threatened Terence, a bit peeved.

''Tis too bloody late,' said Patrick. 'Will ye look at him now? He's off up Tutbury Street chasing that elephant. Hey, how would you like some real adventure, not imaginary and that?'

'What?'

'I'm going out with some men tonight, and we're going to break into Pauldens, and they want me to shin up the drainpipe and get in through the window. And I'm going to nick some real jewels for Vera. You can get a new collar for Raq.'

'I can't,' said Terence. 'Me mam's fancyman isn't coming tonight, with it being Daisy Nook day, and she said I can stay in all night and listen to the wireless.'

'And then what?'

'Well,' said Arthur. 'You'd all been in the lavatory for your cigarettes except Patrick. So I thought I'd sing "In this world of darkness we must shine" just once more, when he runs in and says he's got to have a cigarette 'cos it'll be the last he'll get for a thousand years. Then Constable Donovan shouts to say he knows where Patrick is, and he's got to come out right away, so out he goes.'

'They've given him seven years in the reformatory to the other side of the Mersey in Cheadle. What do they do to you in a reformatory?'

'You get bread and water, and they make you play a lot of football,' said Kevin. 'And you all have to wear the same clothes, and they make you keep clean, and you get the strap a lot.'

'He's ten now, so he'll be out when he's seventeen. What'll he do then?'

'They let you join the army or the navy.'

'Poor sod!'

'It's one way out of Ancoats, anyway,' said Sean. 'Are there any other ways out? I don't fancy bread and water and football.'

'I don't think so,' said Terence. 'Me mam says they think

they're doing us a good turn. She says a kid doesn't need to commit no actual crime. "Where you from?" says the magistrate. "Ancoats," says you. "Right," says he, "seven years in the reform school, and let that be a lesson not to come from Ancoats in future."'

'They gave Dermot six strokes of the birch, and that for just eating chocolate,' said Sean.

'Aye,' said Kevin, 'but 'twas after he'd broken into a toffee shop to get the chocolate.'

'All right, then – so what about Alfie getting five years in the reform school for climbing over a wall to get his ball back?'

''Twas the wall of a tobacconist, the back window had been forced open, there was fags in his pocket, and nobody could find a ball.'

'Sure that's what they call "circumference" or "circumstantial", says me dad.'

As the lads turned into Jersey Street, Vera tapped at them from her window. Then she ran out of the door and beckoned Kevin. 'No, just Kevin on his own,' she specified.

'What d'y'want? I'm going somewhere.'

'Where you off to, then?'

'Rochdale Road, to see the illuminated tram.'

'Will you take me? As your sweetheart? Only I've got no sweetheart since you know who was sent to you know where. And you've got none neither.'

Kevin scratched his backside and twirled round three times in order to think. 'All right,' said he. 'Long as ye don't be telling nobody, and as long as ye don't be taking it serious. D'y'hear now?'

The illuminated tram was the Town Hall's idea. Every time a tram route was changed over to a bus route, the last tram was covered all over with coloured lights, and a gramophone loud-speaker on the front of the tram played 'Happy Days Are Here Again' as it jerked and sparked down the tracks.

Vera gripped Kevin's arm tightly because she said she was afraid of illuminated trams. She also steered him further along the road away from the gang in order to get a better view. The tram car clattered and ding-donged. Hundreds of little lights of all colours reflected in the yellow and red paint. The gramophone played:

What'll I do when you are far away and I am blue,
What'll I do?

The tram car was magnificent, and people cheered. Behind it came a sulking bus, looking sheepish as though it had taken the job from the tram by telling tales.

'And I am blue, what'll I do?'

Kevin and Vera couldn't find the gang, so they walked home together, and Kevin told her how he and Arthur were never going to get married because they were going to go prospering in Canada and find tons of gold; and she asked him what would be the use of all that gold without a sweetheart to spend it on; to which Kevin could think of no answer.

She knew a short cut through an entry, and it was dark, and they fell over a middentin, which rattled. At last there was just enough light from a street lamp to see where the middens were.

'Would you like to kiss me?' asked Vera.

'Yes,' said Kevin, and carried on walking.

'Well, what are you carrying on walking for?' she asked. 'Stop and kiss me.'

He stopped and gave her a peck on the cheek like when he kissed his mother before going to school.

'Call that a kiss?' she sneered. 'I mean a picture kiss. Like this.'

And she put her arms around his neck and gave him a strong endless kiss on the lips, moist lips to sweet moist lips. Her kiss was wonderful and like sliding down the helter-skelter without touching the sides. He didn't know what to do with his hands, so he clasped them on the top of his head. 'And again,' she breathed in his ear. And she kissed him even stronger and more endlessly. This time he held his arms wide like aeroplane wings, and it was like having a second go on the helter-skelter.

'Do you want to put your hand up my clothes?' she whispered, and what she whispered was like sucking hot winter mixture and it frightened him. He didn't know what to do, so he ran away from her as fast as he could, knocking a midden over and making it sound like a cannon, so that a cat screeched and scampered. He ran smack into a lamp post and cut his ear, which began to feel very large and like rubber. And still he ran. Near Saint Anne's he tripped over the edgings and cut both his knees.

He fell into the house breathless, and said he'd been practising the Scouts pace doing a mile in twelve minutes. But his mother knew he'd been fighting, and made him go to bed without the candle.

'What happens when you put your hands up a girl's clothes?' he asked the gang next night.

'You feel her knees,' said Sean.

'Is that all?'

'Me mam says they don't tell you any more till you leave school and get a job,' said Arthur. 'And the Sunday school teacher said it was about birds and bees. I think you're supposed to watch them.'

'Like Romany does,' said Terence.

'There's none of you knows nothing about nothing,' said Michael. 'Sure we haven't the birds and bees in Ancoats, but have we not got the dogs? And have none of ye noticed a couple of them together just before someone chucks a bucket of water over them?'

Kevin's soul blushed at the thought of somebody swilling a bucket of water over him and Vera when she was kissing him, and him with his arms outstretched.

But in bed, he had a more serious problem to contend with. He was now in love with Vera, but what would Betty think up there in heaven? She'd cry. And what would happen when they all met up after they'd died, all three of them? He wished he was back at Saint Anne's, for, though it might be a problem God couldn't answer, he knew Father Sullivan would have a few words to say on the subject.

'Wantums ikkle cuddlums, denums?' asked Mrs Taffy, pulling Sean towards her and undoing his trouser buttons. 'Oh, my goodness! It's still here!' Sean closed his eyes, and once more he joined the warm angels. But a strong desire came to him; he remembered what the gang had been saying about putting a hand up a girl's clothes. He knew he must be bold and brave; he felt it was the next thing a boy was expected to do. He fumbled his dithering hand underneath Mrs Taffy's skirt.

She clouted him hard across the face and sent him spinning into the stable wall. 'You dirty little pig!' she yelled. 'You stinking little bug-ridden Ancoats brat! How dare you, you mucky sod! If my husband knew what you'd just tried, he'd thrash you within an inch of your life!'

'I'm sorry,' blubbered Sean.

'Sorry! I should bloody think so! You'll have to become a man before you get up to tricks like that. Get out, and don't ever come back!'

Sean ran out of the stable. The streets were grey and seemed to spin around and around. People had large heads and said words he couldn't understand. Bicycles wobbled. Motor-cars honk-honked; they honk-honked too loud and the honk-honks hurt his ears. He needed to take a deep breath. He took a deep breath, and tried to hold it. The ragbone man shouted 'Eeeyagbone' and the knifegrinder made blue and red sparks on his big stone wheel. Bicycle bells tinkle-tinkled. More motor-cars honk-honked. He must find the gang; he needed to find the gang. He ran down Palmerston Street.

It was easy to find the gang – it was easy to find everybody, because everybody was going down to the river. The Medlock was in swift fierce flood, following thunder and heavy rain after the heat wave. The river had gone mad. It was already over its banks and lapping into the street. The gang was at the Pin Mill Brow bridge where they could watch the angry brown waters leaping like killer lions over the old mill weir.

'What's happening?' Sean panted.

'The Devil's been squeezing the hills,' said Terence.

The interest of the crowds was directed at the many objects which came swirling down the torrent. There was a clothes basket and a clothes prop trailing a line with some clothing still pegged to it. There was a half-submerged wooden dog kennel. A celluloid duck spun around and around and made the crowd laugh and go '*quack-quack*'. Orange boxes and motor-car tyres were bobbing and twisting and turning. There was an old boot, which people said must have been a good 'un for it hadn't let the wet in. There was a white enamel po, which people cheered. And the splintered half of a sign which said '*will be prosecuted*'. And then, tossing and tumbling over the wild cataract struggled a little white dog, fighting desperately with its front paws. It pawed at a box hopelessly; the box bobbed away. The little dog's paws paddled and paddled; it turned in all directions; a tyre hit against it, and its head went under for a second.

'Tiny! Tiny!' screamed Sean. 'Ye'll not be drowning again! I'll not be letting them drowned ye!' And he threw himself into the callous monster flood. There was an '*Oooooo*' from the crowd. Sean's hands flailed towards the dog. The little dog tried to paddle towards Sean. They both went under the bridge.

'Ach, ye daft little bugger!' shouted Constable Donovan. He ripped his helmet off, dropped it to the ground, and dived into the roaring mud and slime of the Medlock. The dive took him straight under the bridge, also.

Nobody moved. Nobody could move. It was as though nothing had happened. All were staring at the bridge. There no longer seemed to be the noise of wild water. An old woman knelt down, gripping her shawl with her left hand until her knuckles showed white. She made the sign of the cross with her right. '*Hail, Mary, full of grace; the Lord is with thee; blessed art thou among women, and blessed is the fruit of thy womb, Jesus –*' Most of the women knelt down in the mud, and the men took off their caps. '*Holy Mary, Mother of God, pray for us sinners, now and at the hour of our death.*'

They began to repeat the prayer, and some women howled.

'Aw, come on!' shouted Michael, thumping the other lads on the shoulders. 'Let's be doing summat 'stead o' this praying!'

They rushed across the road and jumped to look over the bridge, but all they saw was the tumbling river rushing and making waves against the black-bricked precipices of the mills until the river turned at a sharp bend. They ran along the streets, finding walls wherever they might get a view, and jumping and climbing up them. Rubbish still rushed down with the surge, but there was no sign of Sean, Donovan or the white dog. They asked a man who was leaning outside a factory archway where the river went to.

'How should I bloody know,' he growled. 'I'm not a bloody water rat. It goes under the buildings or summat, into the bloody sewers for all I know.'

'That's it!' said Michael. 'They'll have gone into the sewers. Shout down the grids!'

Kevin, Arthur and Terence rushed to different grids in the gutter. They flung themselves down till their mouths almost touched the bars and called Sean's name as loud as they could. They ran to more grids and more grids, keeping near to the walls and factories which might be fringing the river. There was no access; there were no banks; only steep black factories rising from the water, which nobody could ever climb up.

Arthur pulled and tugged at one of the grids, until he managed to open it. They all rushed to him. But all he had opened the grid for was to rescue a cigarette packet, inside which was a card of 'HMS *Rodney*', a good find, for he was collecting British Warships. It was wet and would have to be dried on the oven top. Kevin thumped him in the stomach.

They put their ears to the grids, but all they could hear were distant waterfalls from down below, dripping and splashing and plonkings; no yell from Sean, no shout from Constable Donovan, no bark from the little dog. At last they were able to see the river again. It ran alongside the huge College of Technology, and part of it seemed to go under the great red building. Then they could follow it no further.

'They're all drowned!' said Michael.

'Aye,' they all agreed.

'We did the best we could,' sniffed Terence. 'And sure 'twas heaps better than just saying prayers, and that.'

Michael pointed to the college. 'That's where they'll be, under the college of science, and 'tis their graves, and isn't that big college some great gravestone for 'em!'

''Tis better than the cenotaph in Peter Square,' agreed Kevin.

'Aye, and better than them marble angels in Moston,' said Michael.

'You can always tell directions in the cemetery,' added Kevin. 'For the green moss grows on the north sides of the angels.'

'What do they do over there in that college?' asked Arthur.

'Science,' said Michael. 'Sums and that.'

'Sean won't like that,' said Terence. 'For he was no good at sums.'

'Not in school he wasn't, 'cos he was tired and went to sleep a lot, and had to wear the dunce's cap,' said Michael. 'But you should have seen him on the milk round. He could do shillings and pence and ha'pennies and farthings in his head without even thinking. And wherever he's gone, he's got a dog with him.'

It was obvious that the lads would be spending the night at Arthur's, and Arthur was pleased and proud. These Catholic micks were forever calling him a Saxon and a bastard, but whenever they were in trouble or upset or needed an alibi, they came to him. He was no leader, and never would be a leader, and didn't want to be a leader. Kevin was his leader and ordered him about and made him share his fish and chips; but on the other hand Kevin told him stories from the books; although on the other hand again Kevin was always giving him the wrong answers in class. Michael wanted him to be a Communist and made him sing 'The Red Flag'. Terence ordered him to be a Catholic when he was playing at being a priest, and he had to make the sign of the cross when Terence said 'dominoes'. Being a Saxon bastard was at times a very important thing to be.

Summer nights were grey for a long time, and they spent the hours playing alleys by candlelight; sometimes they pretended the alleys were soldiers; sometimes they put the alleys in plates and pushed them around the table because they were supposed to be sailors in ships. Going to the lavatory in the yard in the jet black of the night was the thing they were frightened about, and they all went together and held hands with whichever lad was sitting on the seat, for there was a terrible fear among them that Sean's hand would reach up from beneath the lavatory and pull them down into the sewers, because he was lonely.

Evening was the time Father Sullivan liked best, the half-hour before twilight when the church was his. As usual his assistant, Father Granelli, had gone out for a meal with some Italian family or another. He would come back reeking of Chianti, olive oil and garlic, and yapping on about Venice or Florence or some damn place in Italy; then he'd yawn and belch and go to bed. Seamus Sullivan was often tempted to peep through the keyhole of the Italian's bedroom just to see if the man got down on his knees and said a prayer before getting into bed. He doubted it. There were often snores coming from the room before he'd had time to untie his bootlaces.

Father Granelli didn't have his problem. Problem? One problem would be easy, but Father Sullivan had many. The *Manchester Guardian* had told him that Ancoats, which was less than a square mile in area and included a railway station, a river, a canal, and many cotton mills and chemical factories, had a population of twenty-nine thousand souls, most of them being Irish Catholics of one sort or another. And that gave him twenty-nine thousand problems of one sort or another. The same newspaper page had also told him that, whereas most slum areas averaged four people to a house, Ancoats worked out at six to a house, and tiny houses at that, with only two small bedrooms. But his main problem was what to do with the poor-box collection, for all his parishioners were poor yet they gave unstintingly, with a bit of bullying by him, towards people whom they imagined were poorer than themselves. What should he do with that money?

It was all right for Father Granelli to be going out for meals every night, stuffing himself with spaghetti and macaroni and thisie and thatie and rat-a-tat-tatty, but he, Seamus Sullivan, was hardly likely to share a meal with any of his Irish families. Would you know that he'd once called in a house where the husband, wife and kids had been sitting around the orangebox table eating live tadpoles from a bowl?

'Now don't ye be swallowing them alive,' the man had said, 'For they'll grow into frogs in your bellies and eat any other food ye take, and ye'll die of starvation in the course o' time. So chew them now, d'y'hear?'

He knew that Christmas dinners were often delayed a week until the women could walk the long miles to the rich districts in order to mooch through the bins for turkey carcases, thrown-out cake and pudding leavings, for broken toys and torn shreds of crackers which sometimes had mottos for the kids to read. There were some impatient ones who ate Christmas dinner on Christmas Day, but the turkey had often been a cat called a rabbit. There were those who stole food; there were those who stole money to buy food. But suppose he gave poor-box money to any woman who begged for the price of a loaf, sure how many more women would come queueing up outside the church for a similar hand-out? Aye, how many? And wasn't the church falling to pieces, blooming pieces, with the black bricks crumbling away with the soot and chemicals in the air? And when the church rotted to ruins, what would there be in its place? Ach, there'd be nothing! Giving poor-box money to the poor would break and destroy his church. Should the poor-box money then be put into a building fund so that Saint Anne would always have a home in Ancoats and the people's spiritual wellbeing be taken care of for generations to come? 'Twas a problem, and no mistake.

He wandered up and down the aisles, hoping against hope that the statues might give him guidance, just the flicker of a sign. Little Saint Anne there, the mother of the mother of God, the grandmother in name of Jesus. He patted the pedestal. If only she could become alive and get down from her pedestal and cook him a meal. And wouldn't that be one in the eye for Lorenzo Granelli, eh? Liver, kidneys, bacon, sausages, and two fried eggs with golden chips, and salt and pepper, and thick brown gravy, and a mug of strong tea.

'And ye've been stuffing yourself with all them stodgy things done in olive oil that'll bring out the pimples on a man's face till he looks like a leopard of the jungle,' he would say to Father Granelli. 'But ye'll not be guessing, no never in a million years, what a dinner I've been sitting down to this night, nor would ye be knowing the name o' the grand and holy lady as put the pan on the griddle.' And he'd belch louder than Granelli had ever belched. 'Twould be a miracle. And then he remembered to his shame that it was money advice he needed, and that he should not have been thinking such thoughts. He made the sign of the cross by way of apology to Saint Anne, kneeling down to pray before her statue. The church was filled with restful patches of evening shadow, and he could just vaguely hear the voices of little girls playing in the school playground, the only safe place for them to play in at dusk.

> *He loves her, he kisses her, he takes her on his knee;*
> *He says 'now Kitty Mulligan, won't you marry me?'*
> *The wind, the wind, the wind blows high,*
> *The rain comes scattering down the sky.*

He asked himself what had happened to the millions of Irish who had crawled and clambered like ants into England over the centuries, and in particular during the Great Hunger. Where had they all vanished to? In those days there had been a few churches and no schools, and the Irish had lump-sugared themselves into the English cup of tea; lost without trace. There were Englishmen in England who didn't know they were actually Irish. And all because there had been no churches to keep them together. Ach, it was easy for Father Granelli whose Italians formed societies to keep the Italians in order; but he had no help from anybody. He made up his mind that he might do a deal with God. If only he could send one single pure soul to heaven, he would have divine agreement to open a building fund with some of the poor-box money.

While thus meditating, he saw, through the corner of his eye, a boy tiptoe into the church. The boy went to the statue of Our Lady, and began filling his pockets with the candles. 'Hey!' shouted the priest. The lad stood petrified as Seamus limped towards him.

'Oh, Father,' said Michael, 'and 'tis glad I am to see you, and me banging at your door till the house rattled.'

'You're stealing from the church!' shouted Father Sullivan. 'You're stealing candles from the Blessed Virgin herself!'

'No, Father.'

'You're lying!'

'Would I be lying to a priest of holy orders and putting me immortal soul into the greedy paws of the Devil? Aw, sure may God strike me down dead!'

'Then will ye be telling me what you're doing with them candles sticking out of your pocket?'

'Borrowing them, that's all. And 'tis the very reason I was hammering away at your door, in order to get your holy permission, which I knew you'd not be refusing. For now there's a man and his wife and a baby a few doors from where I live and there's not a crumb passed their lips this whole two days, nor have they the pennies for the gas to see with, nor for coal for the fire to cook upon or warm themselves with. Now – and may God bless him – I have obtained some sausages from Mr Fritz, the best pork butcher in the town. And I thought these candles would do for the frying of the sausages and the warming and the lighting of the home. And 'tis only borrowing, for I'll pay the Blessed Virgin back for her candles, you see if I don't.'

Father Sullivan didn't believe him for one moment, but it was a good story; it was a parable which troubled him, and maybe there was some semblance of truth in it. Michael knew he was winning.

'Sure them was powerful words you said in school about Sean, who was drowned, Father. I could never sin again, in case it's my turn next; but 'tis a pity you couldn't have said a requiem for him.'

'Indeed it is,' said the priest. 'And 'tis a great pity his parents could not have afforded the ten shillings for the requiem.'

'If I saved my money, Father, d'y'think you could do a requiem for five shillings?'

Father Sullivan thought for a moment. 'Well, now, I suppose I could, but ye'd not be after telling anybody, because there'd be such a rush on requiems as never there was; and the number I'd be called upon to say would prevent me going about me normal priestly duties.'

'Would a five-shilling requiem be as good as a ten-shilling one?'

'Oh, that it would. I'd not be leaving a single word out.'

'Thank you, Father.'

This lad was a good lad, Seamus thought; almost a perfect lad. He had the natural gifts needed for a priest. Could this be the sign he had asked Saint Anne for? Could this be the soul entrusted to his care?

'Tell me, now,' he said, 'has the notion ever occurred to ye to answer the calling of God's sacred priesthood?'

'Oh, it has, Father,' said Michael, 'it has indeed, and many a time at that; but I think I'd rather grow up to be a Bolshevik.'

Michael made the sign of the cross and walked out of the church. Father Sullivan put his hands to his eyes; he knew the saints were laughing at him and saying 'Silly old Seamus Sullivan!' The blue light from the lamplighter's pole passed the windows. It was sin flying like an evil spirit. Well, sure enough, he'd asked the bishop to send him where there was sin, and there was an abundance of it in Ancoats, which ought to have been called Sincoats.

There was sin even amongst the ugly mills and black buildings. He'd once taken a walk down all the streets in his parish, and there had appeared to him, almost by divine guidance, a building in Mill Street which said 'The Toy Balloon Factory'. That in itself had been all right, but then he'd noticed across the street, and directly facing the toy balloon factory 'The Excelsior Iron Bedstead Works', and he had immediately sensed sin in the closeness of the two factories; there was something evil about the intimate proximity of rubber balloons and iron bedsteads; something he couldn't exactly put his finger on. He had written letters to this effect to the owners of the factories, and had received a five pound note from a Mr Goldberg, and three one-pound notes from a Mr Cohen. As it had been a sin of buildings and not of people, he had decided to start the building fund with the eight pounds.

Another figure came into the darkening church. Came? Well, sort of half-danced, half-stumbled like a drunk. Seamus Sullivan stepped back in the shadows and watched. There was no doubt about it, the man was three sheets in the wind. 'Will ye be on yer way now and not be desecrating the house of God with your paralytic presence!' he shouted, hobbling forward.

The intruder was draped or loosely covered in a torn and stained overcoat many sizes too big for him, and tied with a length of rope. He wore a mud-caked navvy's boot on one foot, and an old carpet slipper held by a pickle-jar rim rubber on the other. His face was smeared with stains as brown as gravy, and it was the ugliest and most twisted face the priest had ever seen. The man's arms twitched from his shoulders as though they were on a loose thread. He was bald, and his jaw hung open.

'And who the Devil might you be?' the priest asked. He sniffed at the man's breath but there wasn't a hint of alcohol in it. The man was ill, and that was for sure. Father Sullivan motioned for him to sit on a pew; he lay down on the pew, stretched himself and put his hands under his head ready for sleep. The priest pondered.

Outside in Harding Street, Michael and Terence were counting the candles. It had been agreed to sell them from door to door as sacred candles blessed by the Bishop of Salford who had once shaken hands with the Pope. The money would then be invested in methylated spirits to sell at a profit to the tramps, in order to pay for a requiem for the drowned boy. 'And would ye know,' said Michael, pleased with himself, 'the old galoot's offered to do a requiem at cut price?' Terence wondered if now wasn't as good a time as any to ask Father Sullivan if he would consider making him an altar boy.

'Faith, and I don't see why not,' said Michael. 'He's in the hell of a good mood. Did he not want to turn me into a priest there and then? And if he could turn me into a priest at the drop of a hat, he'd make you an altar boy quick as winking.'

'Ah, the Lord bless us and save us!' said Father Sullivan. 'And isn't this sacred place becoming more like London Road Station every minute. What d'y'want?' he snapped at Terence.

'To become an altar boy,' said the lad.

The priest growled. 'Have I not told ye before, and a thousand times at that, I'm not able to make ye an altar boy so long as your father's a jailbird? 'Twould be considered an ecclesiastical injustice by all and sundry.'

Terence suddenly noticed the man spawled on the pew. 'That's Rice Pudding, the mad monk!' he spluttered. 'He must have escaped from the Prestwich lunatic asylum. His teeth will grow at full moon. Shall I run for the new policeman, Father?'

'You'll be doing nothing of the kind, and it isn't the man you say it is. Monk indeed!'

'Oh, but it is, Father. Haven't I been close to him many a time when we've been squirting water pistols, for you have to get near to squirt a water pistol in the face; 'tis not like throwing half a brick.'

'Will ye cock your ears, me boy, and hearken to what I'll be telling you now. For this is not a monk. Nor will you be galloping off to the new policeman. What you'll be doing is carrying yourself off to the nuns' house and asking Sister Veronica to be dashing here as soon as she can. And you'll not be breathing a word of this to a living soul, neither to your mother or any of them fine young friends you have, for 'tis the sacred duty of an altar boy to be in the secret confidence of an ordained priest of the Holy Catholic Church.'

'Altar boy!'

'I'm giving it me deepest and most concentrated concentration. But there's them dirty drawings you do –'

'I don't do them any more, Father. I put trousers on the gods.'

'And there's that blooming old wireless set stuffing your head full of nonsense.'

'I only listen to whether there's gale warnings for the Faeroes and Fair Isle, and Big Ben, honestly, Father.'

'Is that so? Well now, haven't I had me eye on you to help serve at the sacred altar? And with there being a vacancy arising in the near future. But you must off and do what I told you, and be minding you keep a secret.'

'Yes, Father. Yes indeed, Father. Indeed I can, Father. And thank you, Father.'

Terence clicked his tongue between his teeth and patted his thigh as though ordering a dog to follow him, and ran out of the church.

Father Sullivan looked for the dog – he even looked under the pews – but couldn't see one. He hobbled to the altar and from behind it brought a large envelope. In it were the birth certificates and marriage certificates of all his parishioners who had died without leaving a known next-of-kin. He always collected these documents; nobody else wanted them; and there they were snug behind the altar, listening to all the Masses and all the prayers and all the hymns; and ready in case they were ever needed should some long-lost relative turn up in the years to come. A Yankee in a big hat had once made a handsome donation when he'd produced the right certificate.

Father Sullivan picked a certificate out of the pile and put the rest back in the envelope, which he hid behind the altar again, then genuflected. Leaning on the pew backs for support, he limped down the aisle, picking up a splinter in the palm of his hand which pained him.

Sister Veronica came into the church. She was a tiny lady and she wore the largest, widest, most stiffly starched hat it was possible to wear without getting taken by the wind and blown over the mill tops like a kite. She reminded Seamus of a swan, and when she walked fast, which she always did, the wings of the swan flapped. Seamus was never sure whether swans quacked or hissed. Sister Veronica was English, and spoke in a posh sort of way.

'I'm thinking now it would be a wonderful thing if you could take this unhappy soul to the Little Sisters of the Poor, for he's in need of the loving care and attention which them blessed saints of ladies devote them lives to,' he told her. She stared at the grinning figure for a minute.

'But he looks like a simpleton, Father. I think he should be in one of those places they have for such poor persons.'

'Sure he's barmy right enough, but there's nothing like a good scrubbing and some clean clothes and a hot meal in the belly to make a man feel less barmy than he really is. I'm sure them Little Sisters will bring out the best in him, for don't they have the patience of saints?'

'Tell me, Father, is he one of us?'

'Oh, that he is.'

'With the greatest respect, Father, I doubt it.' The nun signalled with her hand for the man to get up. He shuffled off the pew and stood facing her. She slowly and deliberately made the sign of the cross. He waved his hand like bye-bye without raising it higher than his shoulder. He grinned wider than ever at her, then he pointed to her hat and laughed, and saliva ran from his mouth.

'That's hardly the response I'd expect from a Catholic,' she said sternly.

'Here's his birth certificate,' said Seamus.

Sister Veronica read it. 'Daniel Donovan,' she said. 'Wasn't that the name of the policeman who was drowned?'

Seamus took the certificate from her hand, stroked his chin, and held the paper near his nose and then at arm's length as he studied it very meticulously. 'Well now,' said he, 'and isn't that a remarkable coincidence?'

'I'm not sure he'll respond to anything,' said Sister Veronica. 'I'm sure he should be sent to Prestwich asylum.' Her manner softened and she smiled a gentle smile at the man. He began swaying in a sort of dance, and tried to sing to her:

Eee ooh ee arfuraze,
Ee olly olly olly ing.

Sister Veronica listened carefully to the tune he was making a noise about. And then she caught on, and sang with him.

In good King Arthur's days,
He was a jolly king;
He turned three servants out of doors
Because they would not sing.

The man nodded and nodded, and was pleased as pleased.

'What's that?' asked the priest.

'It's an English song. One you wouldn't know. Indeed, I'm surprised he does.' But the man was enjoying himself; he started to dance a disjointed dance.

'Iller, iller, iller,' he sang.

'*The first he was a miller,*' sang the nun, and she danced, and Father Sullivan was surprised the swan didn't fly around his church. She also held her skirts and showed her ankles as she danced.

'*The second he was —?*'

'Eaver.'

'*A weaver. The third he was a little —?*'

'Ailor.'

'Tailor. Three thieving rogues together.'

'Eaving ogues ether.'

The nun clapped her hands. 'Very good,' she told him. Then she took the birth certificate back from the priest. 'Oh, I think they might be able to do something with him after all,' she said. 'Come along, Danny. Come with me.' The mad monk followed her obediently out of the church.

'And if you see a dog trying to get in the church as you go out, tell it to go home!' shouted Father Sullivan.

The lamplight was smeared yellowish across the windows. The girls were playing their last game.

I'll tell me ma when I get home
The boys won't leave the girls alone.
Pulled my hair and stole my comb,
But I'll not care when I get home.

Father Sullivan hopped across to Saint Anne and thanked her feet for the miracle which had taken place, overwhelmed with gratitude that he, a celibate man, had given the world one more Irishman, one more Catholic. He knew that by the time the Little Sisters had finished with the man, his soul, like it or not, would have no alternative but to go to heaven. And that, in the priest's conscience, took adequate care of the building fund.

The falling chimneys of autumn

Outside Terence's door, Arthur held the biscuit tin while Kevin grabbed the cat.

'He might come out and cop us,' said Arthur.

'He won't, 'cos the priest is in there bringing him his altar boy's frock,' said Kevin.

'Will he be made into a priest?'

'In time. If God has any vacancies.'

'If he was a priest, would you go to him to tell your sins like you do on Saturday nights?'

'There'd be no point, for Terence knows what sins I get up to, so I might as well stay in the house and say twenty Our Fathers. That's what he'd give me, him knowing the sins.'

'But he sins as well,' said Arthur, 'for isn't having an invisible dog a sin in your religion?'

'Having an invisible anything is a sin. What he'd have to do is denounce the dog on the Bible.' The cat struggled and hissed and bit and scratched. 'Hey, come on,' said Kevin, 'help me get its paws in the tin.'

With more scuffling and scrabbling like it was two cats, they managed to stick one paw at a time in the biscuit tin which was filled with wet sloppy plaster.

'There y'are now,' said Kevin. 'When that dries we'll have a plaster cast of the cat's paws and we'll get our tracker's badge. You can do the same with lions and tigers, or anything.' He put his arm around Arthur. 'When you and me goes prospering in Canada, that's how we'll be able to track bears for food and fur coats, just following the white trail of paw marks after we've dabbed them in plaster, and we'll be able to make sure it's the same bear.'

'But if we've already caught the bear in order to dab its paws in plaster, why do we have to let it go in order to catch it again?'

'Because we'd have to track it. That's the way they catch bears in Canada.'

'They don't look like paw marks to me,' said Arthur, peering inside the tin. 'They're all blobs and smudges.'

'That's 'cos you're lacking in experience. That's why I've been made patrol leader and you're just an ordinary scout. And who was it helped you pass your fire-lighting test by giving you an aspirin bottle of petrol? It was me. And I can tell at a glance they're plaster casts of cat's paws.'

'Only 'cos you held the cat and pushed it in against its wishes.'

'And that was a dangerous thing,' said Kevin. 'Look at the back of me hand, all scratched and bleeding. I'd have done the same if it had been a man-eating lion.'

'Aye, you might,' said Arthur, 'but I'd not have held the bloody tin for you.'

While they were talking, the cat had shaken itself, growled at them, looked daggers at them, and run into the house leaving white plaster blobs from its paws. A few minutes later Father Sullivan came out of the house; his black trousers were mottled with white paw marks. Kevin pretended not to notice the priest, and the priest ignored Kevin.

'He's very fond of Terence's cat,' said Kevin, when the priest had turned the corner out of sight. 'And that cat is very fond of him, or so says Terence.'

Terence came dashing out. 'Did he notice?' he asked with urgency and panic.

'Notice what?'

'His blooming trousers spotted like the measles?'

'He was too busy not noticing me to notice,' said Kevin.

'And he was too busy telling me mam whereabouts on the wall there ought to be a picture of the Sacred Heart to notice the cat purring and climbing over his knees. He just stroked her and said she was a grand little pussycat.'

'He'll think he's been in a snowstorm,' said Arthur.

'And he might at that,' said Terence, 'for his thoughts is miles away, and there's many a time he's walked into a lamp post, and him thinking of heaven and the angels.'

'Oh, he'd be seeing stars right enough then,' said Kevin, putting the lid back on the biscuit tin before Terence could see what was inside.

'Me mam says the cat had been climbing a wall what somebody had just whitewashed.'

'That'll be so,' said Kevin, 'for aren't they the little buggers for doing that very thing?'

'What's in the tin?' asked Terence.

'I'm not telling you. 'Tis a secret.'

'It's part of our training to become prosperers in Canada,' said Arthur.

'What's a prosperer?'

'You go round in dirty old clothes, and you go weeks without food, and it's snowing, and it's raining, and it's freezing, and you find gold.'

'Sounds more like being a tramp,' said Terence. ''Cept they don't find gold.'

'Some of em do,' said Kevin. 'Mr Stevenson has.'

'Who's him?'

'A famous poet, and he's a poor tramp what enjoys bed in the bush and seeing stars and dipping bread in the river – not the Medlock though – and he's become very rich by writing poems about being very poor.'

'Who said?'

'Mr Beaumont said.'

Just then the kid with the club foot dragged himself past the top of the street, and Terence and Kevin instinctively hid in Kevin's doorway, for kids with club feet and stammers and squints were considered to have evil stigmas; they could turn round and put a curse on somebody, and it would be a strong curse, at that.

'No need to worry any more,' said Arthur. 'He's cured.'

'How can he be cured? He's still got his club foot, hasn't he?' said Kevin.

'Easy,' said Arthur. 'Three kids set on him and beat him up yesterday, and he cried for them to leave him alone, so they said he was human after all, and they'd cured his stigma. He won't be able to curse people no more.'

'In that case, let's go and take a plaster cast of his club foot!' But the kid with the club foot slithered away fast. In any case, Kevin and Arthur had better things to do. They were full of excitement at the gossip that the girl with the tortoise-shell glasses from the library had been raped amongst the bricks of the haunted church on her way home. They stared at the heap of bricks which had once been a church, but was now haunted and full of rats. The mass of rubble looked exactly the same as it always looked.

'What's rape?' asked Kevin.

'I don't know,' said Arthur. 'When I asked me mam she said it was what nasty men did to women and little girls; that's all she said. But I believe it was the new policeman what found her, and she was crawling among the bricks looking for her glasses, and he found them with his flashlamp, but they was broken and had to be mended, so he took her to Ancoats Hospital.'

'Sure that's a lie for a start,' said Kevin, 'for they don't do glasses at Ancoats Hospital; you have to go to the Royal Eye Hospital. I know, 'cos that's where I've got to go.'

'Will you have a stigma when you get glasses?'

'No, because I'm a heretic, and heretics can't have stigmas or do curses.'

'The library's shut today.'

'That's because she won't like coming back in case they laugh at her. Everybody would be going in just to look at her.'

The two lads shuffled away, disappointed that there was nothing to see except the usual rubble of the haunted church. They joined Michael who was on his way to take Tobyjug for a walk.

'We'll live for ever!' they sang as they skipped arm in arm up Ancoats Grove, banging on people's doors to the rhythm, and occasionally shouting 'Mr Daddy Longlegs' or 'Old Grannie Witchie' through a letterbox.

Tobyjug was no longer in residence at the Spread Eagle.

'Ah, the ungrateful little bastard!' said Mr Kelly. 'Sure I'll never trust a dog again as long as I live.'

'What's he done?' asked Michael.

'What's he done? Gone off and left me, that's what he's done,' said Mr Kelly, almost in tears. 'And here was all the beer he'd ever want, and all the meat pies and crisps. And didn't I educate the little sod by teaching him to walk on three paws, with the other up, and do the wounded soldier? And to roll over on his back and die for King and country? And wasn't I in the process of learning him to stand on his hind legs and raise his paw to salute the flag? And all the beer a dog could drink.'

'Has he gone on the stage?' asked Arthur.

'Gone off with the boss o' the brewery, he has. That's what he's done. Sure, the big man himself came yesterday on his annual inspection in the biggest and grandest motor-car ye ever did see;

nearly as long as the blooming street, it was. And I introduced him to Tobyjug and told him what a great attraction the dog was; how people came from miles around to see him die for King and country. "Well," says the big feller. "That's just the dog I'm looking for as a pet for my little girls. 'Tis a big house in the wide open country, and there'll be the fields for them to walk him in, and there'll be the finest food as ever graced a man's table. I'll buy him off ye," says he. Says I, "I'd not be parting with that faithful animal for love nor money." Says he, "I'll give ye five pounds." "He'll never come with ye," says I. "In that case," says he, "ye can keep the five pounds." "Done," says I. So he gives me the five pounds, and "Come on, Tobias," says he. Tobias he called him, would ye know that? Tobias, now; is that a name for a dog? Well, the blooming dog just follows him out and gets into the car and sits right next to the chauffeur, with ne'er a glance behind, without so much as a kiss me arse and a thank you. And away drives the big motor-car. And that's the last ye'll be seeing of Tobyjug.'

'I knew that dog when it was a nothing and a nobody,' said Michael.

Blind Andy had taken up his position, and had started to play 'Believe Me if all Those Endearing Young Charms'.

'I'll give you a pound note if you can tell me how many fingers I've got up,' said Kevin to the blind fiddler.

'Get out, ye cheeky little bastard!' snarled Andy. The lads laughed, for baiting Andy could be very relaxing.

'Hey now, come here, will ye?' said Andy. 'Tell me, who is the boy as said that?'

'Me,' said Kevin.

'Well now, ye're a clever boy, so y'are, with the ready wit and that. So will ye tell me what ye see as ye look around? Tell me now, boy!'

'Ancoats,' said Kevin.

'Describe it to me, will ye? For I haven't the eyes.'

'It's streets and houses, and there's chemical works and rubber works and cotton mills and big chimneys.'

'Do ye like what ye see?'

'No.'

'Ah well, of course, I see none o' that.' Blind Andy spread his arms like a windmill. 'This is Tara, and I'm the king's musicianer, and the men who pass me are the brave and noble warriors, and you young boys are princes of the royal blood. Around me are the grand mountains, and beyond are the wild waves of Lyr. Here's you living among the bricks of Ancoats, and here's me with me abode among the world-beginning rocks of Tara. So tell me now, is it you laughing at me, or is it me laughing at you, for 'tis a gift from God to be a blind man in the streets of the city.'

The day passed in this way, and that way, and in such and such a manner; and Arthur and Kevin eventually turned into Tutbury Street on their way home for tea. Every house in the street had people on the doorstep, and that meant something interesting had happened. The only two closed doors were Arthur's and Terence's. Arthur banged on his door, and his mother opened it just wide enough to pull both the lads inside.

A wretched, sobbing, snorting Terence was huddled up on the couch in his altar boy's frock and smock. Arthur's mother put a packet of kali in Kevin's hand and asked him to try and get Terence to eat it, for he'd not eaten a thing all day. Terence smacked the kali out of Kevin's hand, scattering the white powder over the carpet.

'What's up?' asked Arthur, and his mother grabbed both boys by the arm and pushed them into the scullery.

'I think his dad has killed his mam,' she whispered. 'He came out of Strangeways this morning and went straight into the Spread Eagle, and some busybody told him about the fancyman, and he came home and smashed her with the shovel. She was screaming, and we heard everything with the walls being thin. And he called her a dirty whore and everything. And she was screaming, "Please don't hit me!" And he kept banging her with the shovel. And he threw the wireless against the wall, and Terence was screaming, "Leave me mother alone! Please don't kill her." Then the poor lad ran out to fetch the new policeman, and he came with another one, and they handcuffed his dad and had to crack him on the head with their truncheons for he was ranting and raving. Then the ambulance came and drove his mam away, and you could see blood coming through the blankets. Go back in and talk to him.'

'You look smashing in your altar boy's clothes,' said Kevin.

'Piss off!' shouted Terence; then in a sobbing voice, 'I want me mam. Where's me mam? I'll get her the best piano in the world if she'll come back.'

'Don't shout "piss off" to me,' yelled Kevin. Arthur's mother grabbed Kevin and was about to smack him in the face, but her hand stopped half-way. 'Just you watch your bloody language when you're in my house,' she warned.

She offered her Woodbines around, but nobody took one. She offered Terence what was left in the kali packet, but he didn't look at her; so Arthur took the bag and sucked the kali up through the liquorice stem. He made loud sucking noises which caused him and Kevin to giggle. Arthur's mother shook the alarm clock on the mantelpiece because it had stopped; it never really went properly. She said the windows needed cleaning badly. She said the price of potatoes in the shops was shocking. She rattled the alarm clock again.

Kevin saw a blackjack crossing the oilcloth, and was about to squelch it with his boot, when he thought it might be impolite to squash a beetle in somebody else's house. He showed it to Arthur with the toe of his boot, but Arthur let it run under the sideboard.

There was a knock on the door. It was the little nun in the large white hat. 'Come in, miss,' said Arthur's mother. The nun bustled towards Terence and held him against her.

'Oh, you poor little boy,' she said. 'But don't worry, everything will be all right, just you see.' She raised him up from the couch. 'Have you ever been in a taxi cab? No, I'm sure you haven't. Well, I'll tell you what. There's one waiting for you at the door this minute, and I'm going to take you to a very nice orphanage. There are some very nice boys there, and they play football and ping-pong. Can you play ping-pong? I can, but I'm not very good at it.' All this time she was hugging him gently towards the door. 'Oh, and I nearly forgot,' she said. 'I've got a little present for you. Here you are now – did you ever see such nice rosary beads? They're ivory, and from the tusks of elephants. Isn't that exciting? You can say them while we're riding in the taxi cab to that nice orphanage. How about that?'

The nun opened the front door.

'Excuse me, miss,' said Arthur's mother. 'You'll forgive me bad manners, for I should have asked you, and I didn't ask you, and I'm sorry for not asking you, but would you like a cup of tea?'

'No, thank you very kindly, missus,' smiled the nun, and she closed the door behind them.

Arthur's mother grinned at Kevin. 'It's not often I'm called missus.'

'Aye,' said Kevin, 'and it's not all that often a nun is called miss.'

Arthur's mother put her foot up on a chair and lifted her skirt to her thigh to adjust a garter. She hastily dabbed rouge and lipstick on her face. 'My goodness,' she said, 'I've got to hurry. I'm supposed to be meeting a friend at the Wine Lodge.'

'Come on,' said Kevin to Arthur as soon as she'd gone, 'we're scouts and we're kind to animals. We've got to break in to Terence's house through the back door, for his cat'll be locked in. Everybody's forgotten the cat.'

They managed to get into the cold, dark house, and the cat came meowing and rubbing against them. Kevin picked it up. He gripped Arthur's arm.

'Can you feel it?'

'Feel what?'

'Death. It's here in this house.'

'Shut up!'

''Tis nowt to be mithering your head about,' said Kevin, 'for me dad says the dead can't hurt you; only the living.'

Hark, the tiny cowslip bell in the breeze is ringing,
Birds in every woodland dell songs of joy are singing.

Arthur picked his nose. Kevin listened to the song the hall was singing; a sissie song, and in the same category as cuckoos, begone dull care, mermaids, little daisies showing their heads, and dashing away with the smoothing iron. Boring, oh so boring!

'Arthur!' said Mr Beaumont. 'Perhaps you'll leave your nose alone for a few minutes in order to read us your composition on "Where I Live"?'

'Me nose is sore, sir.'

'No wonder. In that case, read it through your mouth instead of your nose.'

'Where I live is very nice and I live in a nice house, and I have lots of nice friends who come to my house when they are in trouble. My best friend is Kevin even though he gives me wrong answers. I have a nice mother. Sometimes the wind blows.'

The wind was indeed blowing; it was blowing very hard and wild, and the classroom windows were rattling.

'Very nice,' said Mr Beaumont. 'Now would you like me to send you to the clinic to have your nose put in a plaster cast, or maybe a sling?'

'No, sir.'

'Then stop trying to pull it apart.' He pointed to Kevin. 'Read on, MacDuff,' he ordered.

Kevin stood up and rubbed his eyes. 'Where I live,' he said, and he looked around to make sure everybody was listening. He noticed one of the boys at the back was looking at cigarette-cards under the desk.

'Please, sir, Jimmy Cathcart isn't paying attention,' he said.

'Pay attention, Jimmy Cathcart!' smiled Mr Beaumont, aiming a piece of chalk at the inattentive boy. And then Kevin cleared his throat and read out his composition.

'I live in Ancoats among streets named after dead lords, and near me is a museum full of dead gods. At the other end of Every Street is my school, where I learn about dead kings. There is too much dead in Ancoats.

'The museum was once a manor house in green fields and was lived in by the Mosley family, who still have an important street named after them. They were very good to the poor people, and gave them places to keep pigs and hens in, and there was fresh fish from the Medlock which is no longer fresh but full of disease.

'Mr John Byrom was friends with the Mosley family, and spent a lot of time at the manor house, and I think it was here at the bottom of Every Street he wrote "Christians Awake" and not at Hanging Ditch like some say. If Mr Byrom was alive today he would write "Christians Go To Sleep" because being asleep is the best time to think about being a Christian, when men and women do not have to think about money for food, and girls being pulled down entries, and boys being stabbed in fights.

'In 1878, Mr T. C. Horsfall and some rich friends bought the manor to turn it into the first art museum. Mr Horsfall said it was because he had asked children in an Ancoats school, and I think it was this school, if they had ever seen a bee or a lark or a dragonfly,

146

and they all said no, and one girl asked him if the red berries on the picture of an ash tree were roses. So he said he would put pictures of birds and trees and all the other things which nobody would ever see inside his museum. He put big plaster statues of ancient Greek men-gods and lady-gods in a room so that the poor people of Ancoats could live a healthy life, and so that the men would not be interested any more in – and this is what he actually says, sir – "the temptations of drinking, sexual licentiousness, the excessive use of tobacco and narcotics and gambling" – and please, sir, I don't know what "licentiousness" or "narcotics" means. I have never noticed any of the men looking at these things in the museum, because they are usually in the beerhouse. And he said it would cost a lot of money but there should be good music, and the same music repeated every night until the people got to know it by heart, like Mr Hall was doing in his college in Greenheys which is near Ancoats and is called Little Germany because of the many Germans, only I think Mr Hall's name is spelt wrongly because they've put an "e" on the end –'

'Hallé!' shouted Mr Beaumont. 'He died about thirty years ago. He was a musician.'

'So's Blind Andy,' whispered Arthur, and was hit on the forehead by a piece of chalk.

'Hallé was a German who was quite happy to become a naturalized Englishman. Have I made a point?'

'Yes, sir,' said Kevin. 'Well, sir, some rich Americans came along to study the poor people of Ancoats and what Mr Horsfall was doing to help them, and they said Ancoats was just like Brooklyn, which is in America, and the people were the same sort of people. And they went back to Brooklyn and built an art museum so that the hungry people could enjoy art and see what cuckoos looked like.

'Where I live, the old women die with their shawls round them, sitting in front of an empty fire grate because they have no money for coal or food or warm clothing. The money which Mr Horsfall spent on glass cases of dead butterflies could have been spent on these dead old women to keep them alive.'

Kevin finished reading. A number of boys yawned loudly, and he had to swing round and threaten to knock them skenning in the playground.

'So you did all that on your own, did you?' asked Mr Beaumont.

'No, sir. Miss Hindshaw helped me. She let me copy things from little books in her desk.'

'So in fact you've been reading books other than those I've given you for punishments?'

This was Kevin's big moment. He nudged Arthur. 'Yes, sir,' he said. 'I like reading books, and reading books isn't no punishment.'

Some of the boys made girl noises; there were whispers of 'sissie'.

'Well then, in future I shall have to punish you by forbidding you to read books, shall I not? And, besides, too much reading is harmful to your eyesight.'

'Yes, sir.'

'And I think I'll take that composition of yours for the time being.'

Just before the home-time bell rang, there was a tremendous crash from somewhere outside. Some thought a train had crashed; others said the gasworks had blown up. When school let out, Kevin had to give Jimmy Cathcart a quick thumping for not listening to his composition; then they followed the crowd down Russell Street. Fire-engine bells were ringing, and ambulance bells were ringing. A big chimney belonging to a derelict cotton mill had tumbled down in the high wind.

A twisted line of bricks, still smoking with dust, had fallen across several houses, slicing and demolishing them; flattening them so that the bricks of the houses had become mixed with the bricks of the chimney. A thousand people were watching.

'One down, and ninety-nine to go!' shouted a man, pointing to the other chimneys in the sky.

'They were just bricks balancing on each other. The mortar had been eaten away years ago. It's been threatening; oh aye, it's been threatening.'

'Anybody dead?' asked Kevin.

'Only one,' said Mr Taffy, who was standing there with his arm around his wife; and she had her arm around him; and people were pointing and sniggering at them for having their arms around each other in broad daylight. 'Some of the families have moved in with others, and some will have to go to the workhouse, for they'll never rebuild those houses,' he went on.

'Who is it? The one?'

Mr Taffy laughed. 'Old Shagnasty the knocker-up. 'Course everybody was at work or in the streets or in school when it happened. But him, the ugly old bugger, he goes to bed once he's got everybody else out of bed. Serves him right, eh? Oh, but it will put up the price of alarm clocks, see if it don't, for there's no one to replace him, see?'

The firemen sat on the bricks and lit their pipes and cigarettes. Conversation became general. One or two beds had been sliced by the chimney, and bedsteads were sticking out through the rubble.

'Hey, you'd better shift them bedsteads,' somebody shouted, 'or the bugs will run away with the bricks.'

One of the firemen salvaged an enamel jerry from under the bricks. He turned it upside down to let the crowd see it was perfectly dry; then he took off his shiny brass helmet and put the jerry on his head, and bowed to the crowd. The crowd applauded. 'It's Kaiser Bill!' somebody shouted.

'And will ye look at that wallpaper?' said a woman in a shawl, pointing to a side of the wall which had been cut by the chimney. 'Sure the silly idiot what put it up has got the roses wrong way round.'

'It's not that,' said another woman in a shawl. 'It's that he's not matched it properly, for if ye look closely ye'll see that the roses is opening up upwards on one roll and opening downwards on the next, so 'tis half a rose pointing up to God's heaven, and the other half pointing down to the ground.'

'And she hasn't blackleaded her grate in a month o' Sundays. Wouldn't I be ashamed to be seen dead in a room with a grate so dirty?'

An Italian ice-cream man came along, puffing and panting as he pulled his gaily painted cart which said, 'Adriano Pieroni. Ideal Ice Cream'. He'd rushed from Jersey Street in order not to miss any trade which might be going.

Some of the crowd began singing, 'I make-a da ice cream to make-a da you scream for-a da ice cream!' The Italian, with his long black curled moustache, lifted his wide-brimmed hat and bowed to the crowd. Some went up with their pennies; and all would have been well, but from the other side of the crowd there rode a man in a peaked cap and a striped jacket, pedalling a tricycle at the front of which was a huge blue ice-cream box that

149

said, 'Wall's Ice Cream. Stop Me and Buy One.' 'Right, now, who wants triangular iced-fruit drinks? Will ye form a straight line for your triangulars? There's plenty for all and sundry!'

The Italian began calling the Wall's man names, and the soldier of the tricycle-brigade called him names back, which gave an unfair advantage to the Italian for he could babble away ten to the dozen in Italian, and nobody, except the Italians in the crowd, knew whether he was using terrible filthy words or saying Hail Marys, whereas the tricycle man had to watch his language to some extent.

Somebody in the crowd shouted: 'Are ye an Ulsterman?'

'Oh, I am that, and proud of it!'

'And do ye wear the riband?'

'Oh, I do that. When occasion demands, y'know.'

Some people moved towards the tricycle man in sympathy; others veered towards the Italian. Kevin nudged Arthur. 'Could be a religious war any minute,' he said. 'And with all them bricks ready-made for ammunition, 'twill be a most holy massacre.'

Indeed, it might have been a massacre; but a man rushed out of a nearby house with an accordion, and began to play, and the Irish in the crowd began to sing:

> *If you're Irish, come into the parlour,*
> *There's a welcome here for you;*
> *If your name is Timothy or Pat,*
> *As long as you come from Ireland*
> *There's a welcome on the mat.*

A couple of the firemen rummaged amongst the bricks and came up with a pair of bloomers and a blue frock; they held them against their uniforms and started to kick their legs up and dance. Most of the Irish now moved towards the tricycle. And then along came the barrel-organ, and the man began to turn out selections from Italian operas. At this stage, with the welcome on the mat being partly drowned by something by Verdi, the Irish began looking menacingly at the Italians, and, oh by God, the bricks were still lying there ready to be thrown. Then somebody gave a cheer, and looking up the street they saw eight stout horses pulling eight thick wooden midden carts, for the Town Hall had got to know about the bricks and had sent every available man and horse to shift them. Kevin's dad was there with his horse and cart.

'Eight carts one behind the other!' shouted Kevin. 'Will ye look at that, Arthur. 'Tis like Julius Caesar invading Britain, or Hannibal crossing the mountains, and 'tis a sight that'll never be seen again.'

'Will ye tell your mam I'll be working all night?' called Kevin's dad. Flares were lit, and the firemen got on the platforms of their fire-engines and drove away. The tricycle man abandoned his tricycle and said he was off for a drink, and he'd finished with ice cream for the rest of his life.

'You're retreating!' somebody shouted.

'Retreating would be if I'd pedalled off on the blooming old tricycle,' shouted the man in reply. 'But leaving your blooming old tricycle where it is and going off to the beerhouse isn't retreating.' And he walked away, shaking his money wallet.

Kevin and Arthur walked away too. 'You're Irish, aren't you?' asked Arthur.

'I think so. Though I'm never quite sure.'

'Well, will you tell me how it is that sometimes some of the Irish want to fight some of the Irish, then sometimes they all stick together and want to fight the English or the Italians, like just now at the tumbling of the chimney?'

'That's summat we should ask Blind Andy, for 'tis him knows all about these things.' They set off for the Spread Eagle, and Kevin looked more and more thoughtful; he even clambered up a lamp post and swung from the arm in order to help himself think.

'Did you like my composition?' he asked.

'It was a lot of words about nowt,' said Arthur.

'Then why did Mr Beaumont keep it?'

'To wipe his bum on. That's all it was good for.'

''Twas a powerful sight better than yours.'

'No, it wasn't.'

'Nice!' sneered Kevin. 'Bloody nice; everything was bloody nice. Even your mother was nice.'

'Well, she is.'

'She's a totty, and does it with men for money. Call that nice?'

'She does it so I won't have to be sent to a home. It keeps us together and pays the rent and buys the food. And I love me mam.

151

'Sides, I bet your mam wouldn't go tottying to keep you out of an orphanage.'

'You're a snotty-nosed Protestant Saxon bastard!'

'And I'll bet your shit stinks if anybody could get near enough to smell it without getting gassed.'

They arrived at the beerhouse when Andy was playing 'Kelly, the Boy from Killane'. He'd chosen this melody because there was nobody inside the beerhouse except a complaining ice cream man; and usually when there was nobody inside it pleased Mr Kelly to hear the fiddler playing about an Irish hero with the same name as himself, and Kelly of the Spread Eagle would supply him with a pint of slops to keep him playing.

While waiting for Blind Andy to finish his tune, the lads listened to the conversation inside. The man was using a lot of filthy words about ice cream, to which Mr Kelly could be heard replying: 'Well now, 'tis like this. Sure the Irish is no good on the ice cream or the barrel-organs; they're best with the bricks. Now them Italians is good with the ice cream, but not a bit of flaming good with the bricks. So go back to the bricks, Paddy me boy; stick to what you're good at.'

'And the English? What are they good at? Give me another pint, and that's the last of me ice cream takings. They'll probably slam me in jail when they find out.'

'Ah, now, that's what the English is good at.'

Blind Andy finished his tune and scratched his leg with the fiddlestick. Kevin told him about the funny goings-on at the fallen chimney, and how there was nearly a massacre.

'If only our ancient druids was alive and kicking today, they'd be able to tell about goings-on at the fallen chimney,' Blind Andy said. 'For, to my way of thinking, 'tis all to do with ceremony. There are days like Christmas and Easter and Whit Week, when Catholics and Protestants respect each other's ceremonies and leave each other alone. But this fallen chimney of yours came right out of the blue and there was no accepted ceremony attached to it. If, now for instance, there was a big chimney to topple every year without fail, then the priests and vicars would get themselves involved with it, and they'd create a chimney ceremony which would be respected by all sides. As it is, there was no ceremony, only the random wind, and nobody was prepared for it, and it only took a couple of ice cream carts to get them at each other's throats.' Blind Andy sighed. 'Ah, we're a most mystical people, so we are.'

Somewhere in the middle of the night, or maybe early morning, Kevin woke up to something which was very mystical, and very frightening. He heard the tapping of the knocker-up's pole on the windows of the street. He also heard movements and singing downstairs at the front door. It was the ghost of Mr Shagnasty; it *must* be the ghost of Mr Shagnasty; it couldn't be anything else! But in fact it was his dad singing:

'Tis sweet to think that, where'er we rove,
We are sure to find something blissful and dear.

He ran downstairs with confidence, for even a ghost would be afraid of his dad. His dad had the horse and cart at the door, and was breaking up half a loaf of bread for Roscoe, and singing all the time; but his voice was sweet and womanly, not like his normal shouting when he was singing.

And to know, when far from the lips we love,
We've but to make love to the lips we are near.

His dad kissed Roscoe on its wide nostrils. Then Kevin's mother opened the bedroom window wide. 'Ye daft galoot, will ye come inside and stop making a bigger bloody fool of yourself than ye already are with that blooming old horse!'

His dad shouted up that it wasn't worth it. They'd only just finished clearing the chimney away, and it was time to start on his midden round, so he'd brought Roscoe home for a bit of breakfast. He winked at Kevin, and whispered, 'He's a fine man is Mr Kelly of the Spread Eagle. D'y'know what he did? Well, I'll tell ye. He comes up with a bucket o' beer. A bucket! Would ye think o' that? And we took turns in picking it up and swigging from it, while the stars was shining in their heavens. And we worked with the strength of twenty men each.'

'I thought I heard the knocker-up?' said Kevin, a bit timid-like.

'Old Shagnasty?' laughed his dad. 'You did that!'

'But I thought he was dead.'

'That was last night. This morning he's alive and tapping away at them windows like a good 'un.'

'But –'

'He was underneath all them bricks, and we got him out just an hour ago. 'Twas the rafters what saved him. But, d'y'know, lad, I'm thinking he's a bit knocked in the noodle.' He tapped his forehead by way of demonstration. 'For when we pulled him out, d'y'know, the first thing he said was that an Afghan had done it. "What Afghan?" says I. "There's no blooming Afghan here," says I, "and I wouldn't be knowing an Afghan if I fell over one," says I. "'Twas a big chimney what fell on you, that's all." "But that's it," says he. "You wouldn't know an Afghan if you saw one, but I would; and they can get up to all sorts of disguises." And the Town Hall clock chimed, and he said he'd have to be off on his rounds, for he daresn't keep them mills and factories waiting. So up he gets and grabs his pole, and away he goes and leaves us standing there.'

All things bright and beautiful,
All creatures great and small.

The Salvation Army band played at the bottom of Snell Street by the high tramp ward wall. Near them, a couple of dogs copulated. The bitch broke away and crawled into the centre of the circle. The dog followed, and they began copulating again.

The good Lord made them all.

The big drummer banged loudly on his drum to frighten the dogs away, but all his drum did was disconcert the rest of the band, and they had to stop, shake their instruments, and start all over again; this time with the women members looking up at the sky, and the men glancing at the two dogs. The people in the houses facing the tramp ward wall were able to stand at the door and watch the Salvation Army, for there would be no collection. The Salvationists never bothered collecting; for one thing, nobody could afford to contribute; for another, if they carried a box with coins in, there would be a good chance of somebody snatching the box and running away with it before they marched back to Star Hall. The people were tolerant. 'Sure they mean no harm,' said one woman. 'And it gives them something to do on Sunday,' said another. Michael, Kevin and Arthur stood watching the band with their arms around each other.

The band marched off to 'Where the saints have trod', and somebody shouted for them to mind and not tread in the dog muck down the street. The three lads were left alone in the street. Well, not alone, for further up Snell Street, by the glassworks, they noticed a group of tramps. One man was lying on the flags; the other two were bending over him. It required investigation, and tramps were always interesting to tease.

The man on the ground had his back against the wall. His eyes were wide open and rolling; a dark trickle of blood oozed down his dirty beard. He coughed, and the blood bubbled from his lips. His legs were wide apart; his hands were limp on the flags. Raindrops began to make starry spots in the dust around his gnarled hands.

'Cheer up, Bill,' said one of the standing tramps. 'Remember what we used to say. "*The Midland Hotel is so common of late, we are forced to reside at th'infirmary gate*"? Give us a bit of a smile, eh, Bill?'

The man coughed again, and the rain, now getting heavier, mixed with the blood and made it run faster into his beard.

'He looks like an Ancient Briton,' whispered Kevin, giving Michael a wink and a nudge.

'Aye, and he smells like one too. He's been messing himself and not using newspaper.'

The boys bit their lips to stop from giggling. The tramps noticed them. 'Fetch a doctor. He's dying,' mumbled one of them.

'There's no doctor in Ancoats, not at this time. Can ye not take him in out of the rain?'

'No point,' said the tramp. 'He'll be dead in a couple of secs, and they don't want dead men in there 'cos they can't chop wood in the morning. Best let some other body in as can chop wood.'

'Is there nowt you can do?' asked Arthur.

'Aye, there is. We can take his boots off and rest his feet. They're good leather and new, what he pinched from outside a shop.'

He took the dying man's boots off, and his companion searched through the man's pockets, coming out with a pound note and a ten-shilling note, which he said would be sent to his next-of-kin. Then the tramps said they'd have to go before the tramp ward gate was locked on them for the night, and they shuffled away, arguing over boots and money. Kevin looked around. There were faces at the window, but nobody was coming out to help.

'Hey, Kevin,' shouted Michael. 'Do summat. He's on the way out!'

'Do what?'

'Say the last rites.'

'I don't know 'em. You say 'em.'

'We've got to say summat,' said Arthur.

The three lads knelt down, and Kevin began. 'Bed in the bush with the stars to see, bread I dip in the river; there's the life for a man like me; there's the life for ever. In the name of the Father, and of the Son, and of the Holy Ghost, Amen.'

'You have nothing to lose but your chains. Amen,' said Michael.

'Hark, the tiny cowslip bell in the breeze is ringing. For thine is the kingdom, the power and the glory, for ever and ever, Amen,' said Arthur. The tramp's head dropped to one side. His eyes were wide open, but they'd stopped moving. He was dead.

'What do we do now?' said Michael.

'I don't know,' said Kevin.

'You're a patrol leader in the scouts,' said Arthur. 'It's up to you to say summat.' Kevin scratched his head and thought.

'As patrol leader of the owl patrol of the 102nd Troop, I say we bugger off quick. The last lot of meths I sold him was turpentine, 'cos I'd told the chemist it was for cleaning a paintbrush.'

The three lads ran as fast as they could into Harrison Street, passing the Salvation Army, who were now playing outside the women's workhouse.

Michael felt he ought to do more for communism than just sell *Daily Workers*, because those who read *Daily Workers* were probably daily workers in any case; he must try and convert some of the daily workers who didn't read *Daily Workers*. It wasn't right that people should be without food, and it wasn't nice for them to line up at soup kitchens, and it wasn't nice for them to die in the street in the rain, especially on a Sunday; it wasn't nice for little babies to be put in small coffins; it wasn't nice for people to cut their own throats, or gas themselves, or drink disinfectant. The world must be told. He decided to paint words on a city bridge for all to see;

words were always being painted on bridges, and people wouldn't go to the trouble of painting words on bridges unless it was useful and converted other people. So, having told his parents he was spending the night with Arthur, and having paid Arthur his penny to be alibi, he set off down Great Ancoats Street with a tin of whitewash and a four-inch paintbrush which he'd found lying outside a mill near a bucket of whitewash when some men were having their butties and beer in a shed. It was a sharp night, a Communist night, for the stars were shining. They shone brighter every time another mill closed down and another chimney stopped smoking. He thought of Karl Marx; he wondered if Jesus would have preferred Karl Marx for his dad instead of Joseph. One of the stars looked almost red. Karl Marx would bring his watch from his pocket, shake it to his ear, look at it, and then tell Michael it was time to go and paint words on the bridge. In fact, he'd even copied out some words of Karl Marx, and he knew the old gentleman would have reached in his pocket and given him sixpence to buy a working-man's cap, if he were alive.

By the time he'd dreamed these dreams, Michael was on the Victoria Bridge. It was quiet apart from a gas lamp spluttering, and he walked across the bridge once or twice. He was no longer the nephew of Karl Marx; he was the acclaimed leader of the combined English and Irish workingman's revolutionary brigade, and he had to capture the bridge to rescue the Jewish and Ukrainian working-men in beleaguered Cheetham Hill. The enemy was about to blow the bridge any minute, and they had dozens of machine-guns on the other side. But Michael was fearless. He would get killed of course, but, resting on one dying elbow and pointing to the enemy, he would shout '*Veeva!*' as the citizen brigade jumped over him to victory.

He dipped his brush into the tin. He was about to write the letter W. Then a bus with dazzling headlights turned on to the bridge. Michael ran into the urinal at the end of the bridge, spilling whitewash over his clothes, frightened. He must wait until all was quiet again. He looked around the tiny urinal: there was only room at the tiles for three men, or possibly five boys. It had two entrances, but no door or gates. What intrigued Michael was that the wall had a row of large, fierce-looking iron spikes. He couldn't think why the wall was spiked. With two entrances, and naturally being open day and night, there would be no need for anybody to be so desperate as to have to climb over the wall into the urinal; the same if they wanted to leave; and nobody would burgle the urinal because there was nothing to burgle. All he could think was that the spikes were to stop women from climbing up the wall to look down on the men.

He peeped out, crept out, and dipped his brush once more. This time it was a train in the station. It gave a sudden hush and rush of steam; it whistled; its iron rods clanked; its wheels squealed on the tracks. It sounded like a bad giant, breathing hard with murderous anger. Within seconds he was back in the urinal, which now filled up with engine smoke like a lot of incense in a tiny church. This time he prayed: 'Dear Jesus, please help me to become a good Communist.'

And then he received an inspiration. It was almost as if Jesus had talked to him. He would never be able to write 'Workers Arise'; it would take too long with all these repeated attacks from buses and trains. He would have to shorten his message, and he decided it would be simply '*Stalin*', for everybody knew that Stalin was in favour of the workers arising, and Stalin wasn't the kind of man who would allow poor families to live up at the soup kitchen and men to die in the street. '*Stalin*' it would be.

It was a long and difficult task. There were more buses and trains, there were taxis from the trains, and there was a railway-man on a bike with a red flag sticking sideways from the saddle. Michael was so frightened at times that if a man had been going into the urinal through one entrance and a man going out through the other, he would have been forced to climb the wall, spikes or not. At the finish he was quite white with paint, and he went home down the unlit streets to avoid being taken for a ghost by a policeman or a burglar or anyone else who happened to be roving in the night.

As always when Arthur was being alibi, the door was left off the bolt. He rushed in, woke Arthur up from underneath the coats, and they lit a candle to warm their hands by.

'Is it snowing?' asked Arthur, rubbing his eyes.

'No. But it's freezing.'

'You're covered in snow!'

He was covered from head to toe in whitewash, and it was of great concern to him what his mother would say or, worse still, do. He thought at first it might be a good idea to say that Arthur's mother had asked him to whitewash the backyard when the moon was full, but he realized his mother would demand new clothes from Arthur's mother. Then he remembered there was a notice outside the University Settlement to say men's, women's and children's clothes were going free there. First thing before school he would call in and get some boy's clothes; he could always tell his mother that Sean's mother had given them to him, with them not being required any more and that.

Before nine o'clock, he walked into the Settlement. The floor and tables were heaped with clothes. A student wearing a striped tie with worms on it fixed him up with a swanky suit of clothes, but Michael insisted the student keep his old whitewashed clothes, for they'd clean up beautifully with turpentine.

'You're my first customer,' said the student. 'In fact my only customer. I can't understand it; these clothes have been here for a week, and nobody has called. And yet most of you are going around in rags. Why? What's it all about? These are good clothes.'

'Charity,' said Michael. 'The people don't want charity.'

'If that's how they feel, I might as well arrange for the clothes to be taken away.'

'No, master, don't do that!'

'Then what do you suggest?'

'Leave the catch off one of your windows, and I'll spread the word there's a window open, and – may the Lord strike me down dead, sir – you'll find all them clothes gone tomorrow morning.'

'But that's stealing.'

'Yes, master.'

'You mean they'd rather steal the clothes than just walk in and take them away?'

'Yes, master. Wouldn't you? Y'see, stealing things isn't easy; you have to do something to get something, and if you get nabbed you go to prison, so that's like working and taking a chance at the same time. But charity is just holding your hand out, like you wasn't as good as them what's giving, and saying "thank you, sir" and "thank you, miss" and that.'

'If I leave a window open, they'll steal the entire Roundhouse.'

'No, master. That piano's no good to them; nor that picture of the clown, nor that picture of them hills. And them coloured electric lights what you've got on the stage is no use, for we've only got gas. But warm clothes is needed, for 'tis getting near winter.'

As he was about to leave, he noticed a red fox fur on the heap.

'Would it be all right, master, if I took that fur to go round me mother's neck, for 'tis a terrible cough she's been getting of late?'

Michael left the Settlement with the fur wrapped in brown paper. He was puzzled. People who went to university were supposed to be the brainiest people in all the world, and yet that student couldn't understand the difference between charity and obtaining things.

The cuckoo is a pretty bird,
She singeth as she flies;
She bringeth us good weather,
She telleth us no lies.
Cuckoo! Cuckoo!
Cuckoo! Cuckoo!

The singing came from the hall. The sky was as dull as dishwater, and lights were being lit. The class waited for Mr Beaumont; they guessed he was walking in the cellar playground to smoke a cigarette. Somebody had once seen him doing it; but it was no use writing a secret letter to the headmaster because the headmaster also took turns in smoking in the cellar. It seemed a waste of time putting cigarette smoke in the air when it was already full of stinks from the gasworks, the rubber works and the chemical factory; there was enough to occupy Mr Beaumont's lungs. And of course the injustice of it all was that he caned any child he caught smoking in the cellar or the lavatories.

When he returned to the classroom, he took a piece of chalk, breathed on it, and wrote, 'Anselm. Lanfranc. Becket.' on the board.

'What have those three names got in common? Hands up!' No hands went up, and Mr Beaumont looked around the class. 'My word, I have got a lot of smartly dressed pupils in here today.' This was true, for nearly half the class was better dressed than it had ever been before. This annoyed Kevin, for he was usually the best-dressed kid in class; true, most of his clothes came from the middens but his mother spent half the nights washing and patching and darning them, just like his dad spent a lot of time on the last, cobbling away at old boots for him. He was peeved that many of the kids he disliked most were smartly dressed, even though a lot of their clothes didn't fit. It was something he'd have to punish Arthur for; after all, Arthur existed to be punished by him.

'Right,' said Mr Beaumont. 'Then who's the first victim? Arthur, how about you? Anselm, Lanfranc and Becket?'

'They all play for United,' whispered Kevin behind the back of his hand.

'They all play –'

Kevin realized Arthur would get the strap for being funny. It might be going too far; anyway, Arthur wasn't too well dressed for he had a bit of shirt sticking out through a hole in his trousers. 'Canterbury!' he whispered, a little louder than before.

'They all play for Canterbury, sir,' Arthur answered, though with a puzzled sort of frown which gave the impression he wasn't sure the answer was correct.

Mr Beaumont strode between the desks. 'Kevin, on your feet. Hold your hand out!' he shouted, and Kevin received one mighty whack – slash – across his palm with the ruler. 'As Arthur is presumably your pal, at least according to one of his compositions, I'm sure you won't mind taking his punishment for him.'

'I'll bloody kill you when I get you outside,' Kevin whispered to Arthur as Mr Beaumont walked back to the blackboard.

'In 1093, Anselm was made Archbishop of Canterbury,' said Mr Beaumont, writing 1093 against Anselm. And then he smiled to himself. 'I'm sure I don't know how any of you will become good plumbers or streetsweepers or window-cleaners, or whatever you'll become, without knowing that little piece of information.'

The singing in the hall stopped, and another song was started. Mr Beaumont listened to it.

In Manchester, this famous town,
What great improvements have been made, sirs;
In fifty years 'tis mighty grown
All owing to success in trade, sirs.
For see the mighty buildings rising,
To all beholders how surprising;
The plough and harrow are now forgot, sirs;

> *'Tis coal and cotton that now we've got, sirs.*
> *Sing heigh-ho, sing hey-down gaily,*
> *Manchester's improving daily.*

'Aye,' whispered Kevin to Arthur, 'specially since they've built the new shit-house in All Saints.'

'Hands up those who are proud of this city?' Mr Beaumont asked.

'Not me,' said Jimmy Cathcart from the back. 'There's too many blooming immigrants. They should go back to where they come from, sir.'

'In 1800,' began Mr Beaumont, 'the first city treasurer was Charles Brandt, a German immigrant. He found the money to build drains and roads and put gas lighting in the streets. Later, when Manchester was without money because of its support of Abraham Lincoln in the Civil War, a group of German immigrants got together and helped finance the University of Manchester; they caused it to be built. So the Germans might justifiably call this a German city. The thousands of Italians have filled the drab streets with music and colour; they've opened restaurants; they might say this is an Italian city. Walk up Cheetham Hill Road any night and if you look down into every cellar you will see Russian and Polish Jews sewing garments, sometimes all through the night, on their sewing-machines. Might they not consider this to be a Jewish town –'

'Please, sir,' interrupted Kevin, 'what about us micks?'

'The Irish have been coming to Manchester for three hundred years. Their muscles and tenacity built the first railway station in the world, in this town. Against impossible odds of marshes and swamps they put the first ever railway line from here to Liverpool for Stephenson's Rocket to pull passengers on. Right now, they're building a magnificent library in Peter's Square, where Peterloo took place. In the Great War, which isn't all that long ago, the Manchester Regiment was recruited almost exclusively from the Ancoats Irish – yes, the Ancoats Irish. So the Irish may claim this as an Irish town. Things are changing. Ancoats won't always be the murky ghetto it is today; and those changes, when they come, will have been brought about by the sons and daughters of the immigrants. Yes, Manchester's improving daily.' Mr Beaumont threw his chalk in a good-natured way at a boy in the back row. 'And that's probably a better history lesson than Anselm, Lanfranc and Becket.'

'They sound more like Egyptian sand-shuffle dancers on the music hall,' whispered Kevin.

About the same time, Michael was having a similar lesson from Mr Rocca, who had also passed comment on how well dressed some of the boys in the class were.

'What do you know about Saint Thomas à Becket?' he asked Michael. Michael snapped out of his dream of fighting the rich.

'Please, sir, he was a saint.'

'And I'm sure that you are about to add that his name was Thomas à Becket?'

'Yes, sir,' said Michael, pleased with himself.

'For that wealth of information, you can stay behind after the bell and collect the pens, clean the blackboard, and dust down the statue of Saint Bede.'

'Oh, and please, sir,' said Michael in a desperate attempt to redeem himself and escape the jobs, 'he was shot dead for saying Mass.'

'And when you've done those jobs, you can report to the caretaker to help him empty the wastepaper-baskets.'

'Thank you, sir.'

'Shot for saying Mass indeed!' sneered Mr Rocca. 'Perhaps this'll be a lesson for you in future to get your facts right.' Mr Rocca softened up and smiled. 'There was a piece in last night's paper,' he said, 'where the reporter had set out to amuse the readers. It seems somebody had painted the name "Stalin" on a railway bridge –'

Michael felt his toes curl up in his boots. Did Mr Rocca know? Was he going to tell him that after he had emptied the wastepaper baskets he would be shot for being a Communist?

But Mr Rocca continued, 'The S was the wrong way round, and so was the N, which apparently is a Russian E. So the reporter asked if the Russians had landed in England. Were they about to take over the Town Hall? Amusing perhaps, but doesn't it show how we must be careful with our lettering and our spelling and getting the facts right, unless we wish to be seen and laughed at as clowns?'

The school bell rang, and it shouldn't have rung, for it wasn't a change of lessons and it wasn't home-time. Michael hoped it was a fire and that the school would burn down to the ground, destroying all pens, blackboards and wastepaper baskets together with the statue of Saint Bede, for Mr Rocca was always saying, 'I wonder what Saint Bede would say about your bad writing, or getting your sums wrong, or coming late, or having a dirty face, or flirting ink pellets,' and things like that. For a split second, Michael wondered what Saint Bede would have said about him writing 'Stalin', and with letters the wrong way round.

The little nun with the big white hat rushed into the classroom, and whispered something to Mr Rocca, who went white and made the sign of the cross. Then the little nun turned to the class.

'Children, I have to tell you the heart-breaking news that Father Sullivan has passed away, God rest his soul,' she said. 'His body has just been found in the church at the foot of the statue of Saint Anne, may she pray for him. So kneel down on the floor and say your prayers with her for the soul of Father Sullivan.'

From other classrooms the half-babbled, half-chanted Our Fathers had already started. Michael suddenly had an inspiration. He remembered how his father had always made him readdress letters which came through the door and were typewritten, because typewritten letters were usually from the Town Hall and were dangerous. He decided to readdress the school prayers.

'Dear Jesus,' he thought, knowing full well that Jesus could hear a silent prayer, 'I know that Father Sullivan has just arrived with you, and he must be feeling nervous not having been there before, but, being a priest, there is not the shadow of a doubt that his soul is happy for ever and ever. So I would like to address all the prayers what are being said this minute to Sean, what was drowned in the cut. You know that I kept trying to save money for a requiem Mass for him, and even though Father Sullivan, rest his soul, offered me a cut-price Mass, I never managed to save the five shillings, even with keeping the money what my father gave me to put bets on with, knowing that he never won. But I never got the five shillings, because things kept cropping up, like cigarettes. I hope that Father Sullivan enjoyed a happy death. In the name of the Father, and of the Son, and of the Holy Ghost, Amen.'

Father Sullivan had indeed enjoyed a happy death. He had died in triumph for himself and his little church. Having been so successful in spotting a sinful relationship between the balloons and the bedsteads, he had scoured the town for other buildings which might be in a situation of sin. It was as though the good Lord had guided his steps, for, crossing Pin Mill Brow one day, he came across the Ivy Blouse Mill and the Supreme Shirt Factory facing each other across a narrow passageway called Dark Lane. Shirts, blouses, and Dark Lane! He thanked God for this revelation, and he wrote to both factories pointing out that blouses and shirts and Dark Lane might lead innocent people into thoughts of wickedness. Two typewritten replies, signed by a Mr Hollingworth and a Mr Cockcroft (English this time, and probably Protestants), contained cheques for five pounds each; both arrived with the same afternoon post. This was wonderful, and it pointed the way to the future; buildings could pay for his building, and the poor box could safely be used for the poor. He put his best clothes on – even his top hat, only used for ceremonial occasions – and walked down the church to show the cheques to Saint Anne and thank her. He raised his hat to the statue. And it was then that he dropped to the floor with a stabbing pain in his chest, and everything went purple, then black, then dead.

Kevin told the news to his dad that night with a smear of sadness. He would have liked to look at the priest lying in his coffin, but knew that he would not be allowed; for that matter, it had been a long time since he'd been allowed in a house to look at a body, with him being the heretic boy. 'You're not welcome,' they would say, and slam the door in his face.

''Tis been a long time since I've looked upon the face of a corpse,' he complained to his dad. 'And I miss the cake that went with it.'

'Aw, sure you're not the only one,' comforted his dad. ''Tis a terrible thing at times, is this excommunication business, for I've not been invited to a wake this past six months, and that's an awful lot of free beer I've missed. Looks like the next wake I'm at will be me own, if I live long enough.'

It was Saturday night. Kevin and Michael had settled down in Arthur's house. Arthur's mother had left them a handful of herbal cigarettes which somebody had given her in the Wine Lodge, but which she didn't like very much.

The herbal cigarettes smoked warm and comfortably in the chest; they had a taste similar too, but better than, hot buttered muffins; they made the lads feel relaxed, yet at the same time strong and powerful; there was a safe and secure, pleasant, vibrating freedom in the curling grey smoke rings. It made them as happy as the Christmases they'd never had, always wished for, never would get; Christmasses which nobody would ever get. They gave colour to the imagination, like colouring in a painting book.

'I suppose God made these cigarettes,' said Michael. 'They feel as though God made them.'

''Course he did,' said Kevin. ''Cos they're herbal, and God does anything what's herbal. Herbal is what he likes doing best.'

'So do witches,' said Arthur.

'No, they don't, they do frogs' legs and owl shit, and that isn't herbal.'

The three lads smoked more herbal cigarettes, then lapsed into a contented silence for half an hour, or maybe an hour, or maybe two. Then Michael had a brainwave. He remembered he had Constable Donovan's helmet hidden away at home; he'd kept it as a souvenir because he'd liked Constable Donovan, with all the policeman's faults. It seemed a good idea this Saturday night to put the helmet on the head of one of the statues in Piccadilly; it would be brave and daring; it was, on consideration, the only natural thing to do with a policeman's helmet. The lads were feeling brave and natural.

The first statue in Piccadilly was Wellington, which had lady Britannias on every corner. There were also stone carvings of soldiers in top hats sticking bayonets into other soldiers. Mr Wellington stood very high above them all. At first the lads were shy about standing on the stone steps of the statue; they had a fear that one of the sitting-down Britannia ladies might reach out a long arm and grab them and put them across her knee and tan their backsides and turn them into stone, where they would remain for evermore. But they grew brave, and limped as though wounded, with one foot on the top step and the other on the step below, and sang their own words to 'The British Grenadiers'.

There was a jolly Scotchman at the Battle of Waterloo,
The wind blew up his petticoat and showed his toodaloo.

Then they ran to the immense statue of Queen Victoria. It was agreed that it might be an act of great treason to put the helmet on

166

her head; not only that, but she had a big crown on a big head which the helmet wouldn't go over; and, to hell, she was far too high and slippery. So they contented themselves once more by doing the hippety-hoppety ritual on the steps at the base.

His toodaloo was dirty, he showed it to the Queen;
The Queen was so disgusted she made him scrub it clean.

With a yippee and a wahoo they raced to the next statue. This had no steps and no Britannia ladies: the man stood on his own on a base which said 'Peel'. They danced around it like Red Indians.

Peel's view halloo awakened the dead,
When he found that his hounds
Had been shitting in his bed.

'Ah, now wait a minute,' said Kevin. 'This isn't the ye ken John Peel, or there'd be stone foxes and stone dogs. It's another Mr Peel.'

'Perhaps it's his dad?' said Arthur.

'Who cares?' said Michael. 'He's got a head what'll fit this helmet.'

Arthur had to arch his back with his head against the base of the statue. Kevin jumped on Arthur's back, and crouched like a frog. And Michael took a long run, sprang from Arthur's back to Kevin's back, and was able to clutch Mr Peel's trousers. It was slippery and dangerous, and Michael expected quite merrily to fall and split his head open splosh on the flags a million miles below. But he clung to the statue with hands, knees and boots, with the helmet on his own head, which he at last transferred to Mr Peel's head with the chinstrap under the chin. Then he slithered down, and away they ran. 'We'll live for ever!'

Kevin took a quick look round to see the statue with the helmet. 'Manchester's improving daily!' he yelled. 'Yahoooo!'

With plenty of chalk, which they always carried in their pockets, they chalked dirty words on houses on their way home; really dirty words, filthy words; words which they knew they'd get the cat-o-nine-tails for if they were copped.

The compelling urge to smoke another herbal cigarette got the better of them once they were back in Arthur's. The cigarettes gave them yowling dreams of hungry dragons, falling chimneys, dogs drowning, and the ghost of a priest wafting incense from a censer and making bugs drop from the wallpaper.

'So what have you in that sack, eh? A dead cat, eh? Only this morning I say to myself, "Ikey, what you have not got is a dead cat." I say, "Ikey, what you need is a dead cat."'

'Ar, then you're wrong, Mr Mo,' said Michael, patting the sack. 'For if this is a dead cat, then I'm a dead mouse, and sure I'm not a dead mouse.'

'Then what is it? Not that I wish to know.'

Michael opened the sack and spread a red fox fur on the counter. Ikey Mo stood away from it as though it carried the plague; then he shrugged his arms and addressed a picture of 'Shoeing the Bay Mare' which was high up on the wall. 'Abraham, Isaac and Jacob! Take us the foxes, the little foxes that spoil the vine.' He looked back at Michael. 'That was said by King Solomon, who was the son of King David, and he was a wise man, and he knew a good fox from a bad fox. And he would have said this was a bad fox. It was probably the fox he was talking about, for this fox is three thousand years old. It is a fox which would spoil anybody's vine. Look at the fur; falling out in handfuls. Look at the lining; torn and rotting and eaten by moths. Look at the tail; hanging by a thread. I would prefer you had brought me a dead cat.'

'If it belonged to King Solomon,' said Michael, 'then it must be very valuable as a holy relic.'

'It belonged to one of the ladies of the University what sent bundles of clothes, and was stolen when a window was left open. I want no stolen articles, thank you very much.'

'God's honour, I promise I was given this fur before the window was left open,' pleaded Michael, and he told Ikey Mo about the student, and how the student couldn't understand that it was better to steal than beg for charity.

'And I agree with him,' said Ikey Mo. 'For I cannot understand you people. You starve, you die with diseases, your clothes are rags; and what do you do? You have your magnificent processions at – what is it – Whit Week?'

''Tis called the scholars' walks,' explained Michael. 'And the

Protestants walk to the Town Hall on Whit Monday, and we walk there on Whit Friday, and we cheer each other.'

'And your parents get into serious debt to buy smart uniforms and gay but thin little frocks, so that you can carry banners through the streets for a couple of hours. Then they line halfway up Every Street the Monday after to put their clothes in pawn with me. Hoy, what people!'

'You wouldn't know, 'cos you're a Yid,' said Michael, innocently and politely. 'What's it like being a Yid?'

'A Yid! A sheenie! A Jew! A Hebrew! Oh, yes, I'm all those. But tell me, mouse, what it's like being a mick?'

'Not very nice,' said Michael. 'Once you cross the road out of Ancoats, people look down on you and call you names and make fun of you. You only feel safe in Ancoats.'

'Then that's what it's like being a Yid. Only the people I belong to stay in the boundaries of Cheetham Hill.'

'D'y'mind being called a Yid?'

'Like you, we get used to being called anything. But does it matter when you close the door at night, eh, mouse?' Ikey Mo slapped a florin on the counter, and put the fox fur on a shelf behind him. 'But in a few days I shall be called a Hebrew.'

'Why?'

'Because tonight I am shutting the shutters.' Ikey Mo looked up at a picture of 'The Last Watch of Hero'. 'Ah, you look sad, *shaney madel*. Sad that I am leaving you, eh?'

'I'll speak for her, and it's sad I am,' said Michael. 'But where would ye be going off to, if you leave here?'

Ikey Mo reached under the counter and brought up a pot figure of a shepherd. 'Tell him, shepherd; tell him I go to live with my son in Dresden, which is a beautiful city, and which is where my son has a fine shop where he sells many such figures as yourself and much pottery at good prices; where my grandchildren feed the swans; where I shall no longer be Ikey Mo the sheenie pawnbroker, but a Hebrew with a name you could not pronounce.' He handed the figure over to Michael. 'Here, take this shepherd and look after it; never part with it; it is valuable.' He laughed inside his beard. 'But the man who bought my business did not even bother to look at it.'

'D'y' mean it?' asked Michael, hugging the little statue.

'Take it,' said Ikey Mo. 'It's yours.'

'I'm beholden. I'll call it Ikey Mo.'

'Call it David, for such a shepherd was David. And then he became a great king.'

'I think Karl Marx would rather him have stayed a shepherd.'

'Karl Marx? Karl Marx? Who is this Karl Marx? Get out of my shop before I change my mind!' Michael was about to rush out of the shop, when Ikey Mo beckoned him back. 'Eh!' said Ikey Mo, and he ruffled Michael's hair. '*Shalom*!'

'Oh, indeed I shall,' replied Michael, not sure whether it was the correct answer or not.

Michael now thought that the shepherd he owned was better than all his tram tickets beneath the bed, because it was a real-life peasant named David which he could wash and pretend to feed, and allow to look through the window by day, and stand by his candle at night. But he wouldn't destroy the hundreds of tram tickets, for he was their president and had to be responsible for them in sickness and old age. What he would do would be to let the shepherd stay under the bed with them for a day or two so that the spirits of his tram tickets would merge into the china shepherd like in Holy Communion, or the other way round. Every Saturday night he would let David lie flat on his copy of the *Daily Worker* so that he could read it after he'd blown the candle out and gone to sleep. David could go out with him on Saturday nights and watch the big rollers of the *Daily Express* rolling, and see the ponies and traps galloping out to the stations with the newly born papers; David could fit in his pocket when he went to the teetotal tavern for lentil soup. He would show David all of Ancoats.

What's more, he'd got himself a florin which would help towards some herbal cigarettes.

Kevin, Arthur and Michael were caught by Miss Daly good and proper. They went in her shop quite innocently for a loaf of bread. After standing a few minutes, she came wearily out from the parlour. 'Just resting me weary bones,' said she, and she continued before they could ask for the bread. 'Now tell me, which is Mr Luciano and Mr Diamond and Mr Schultz?'

The boys looked bewildered. 'Oh, I've not forgotten,' she went on, 'the way you used to rob me and my little shop when you were a gang. I've heard all that picture talk of yours when you've been playing at the back. But you're not a gang any more, are ye? The boy who led ye is now where he belongs, is he not? Well, then, I kept a little tally of what you stole, and it amounts to two pounds, so I'll thank ye to let me have that amount by Saturday dinnertime, otherwise I shall have a few words with the new policeman, and ye'll no doubt be joining your little friend in the reformatory.'

The lads left the shop in a daze, for two pounds was more than a man's wages for a week. 'I'll bet the King of England wouldn't have two pounds in his back pocket if he was stopped suddenly,' said Michael.

'We could rob a bank,' suggested Arthur.

'Ach, ye daft ha'porth, we'd need gats and a getaway car,' said Michael.

'And we'd also need a bloody bank,' said Kevin, 'for there's none within a hundred miles of Ancoats.'

Saturday morning arrived, and they'd not a brass farthing between them. The high walls of the reformatory school loomed tall in their imaginations.

They mooched into Raglan Street, where the barrel-organ was playing 'When Irish Eyes are Smiling'. A group of little girls danced around the organ, but there was one little girl leaning against the wall and just smiling. She couldn't dance with them; her one leg, which was shrivelled and small due to rickets, was in an iron leg-frame. It gave Kevin an idea.

'How would ye like to earn a lot of money?' he asked her.

'Oooh, yes, please,' she answered.

He told her his plan, which was for her to knock from door to door with a cardboard boot-box in her hand, and say she was collecting for a wreath. He and his pals would keep a safe distance to protect her from anybody who tried to snatch the box. He told her they themselves daren't be seen, for they were known thoughout the neighbourhood, one being a heretic, one a Protestant, and the other a Communist; but they'd protect her.

'But suppose they ask who it's for?' asked the little girl.

'They won't,' said Kevin, 'they never do. They'd never admit they didn't know who was dead, for it'd be like confessing they didn't know what was going on in the world.'

Arthur ran back for a cardboard box, and in no time they were patting her on the head and telling her to get started. Michael was a bit worried about her having a stigma, but Kevin assured him that there was no such thing, for only a month ago the kid with the club-foot had asked him and Arthur if he could join the Scouts, and they'd said yes; and although the kid was definitely no good at the Scouts pace and tracking, he'd turned out to be very good with morse code and semaphore.

'But suppose they *do* ask who it's for?' the little girl kept repeating.

'Say it's for yourself,' shouted Kevin, losing his temper.

They gave the little girl a push, even threatened to thump her if she didn't get started, and away she went up and down Taunton Street, Tetlow Street, Broughton Street and Copestick Street. They checked her box, and, lo and behold, but didn't she have two pounds and one shilling? They grabbed the money and left her the shilling in the box.

'You said I'd earn a lot of money,' she almost sobbed.

'And am I not keeping my word?' asked Kevin. 'For we've learned you how it's done, and we're leaving you the box with a shilling in it to get you started, so you can carry on, for there's a million streets.'

Well, the lads cleared their debt, and that settled Miss Daly's hash for her, and the Saturday continued as all Saturdays did.

Michael missed Mass the next morning. He'd decided to smoke a few herbal cigarettes in the ruins of the haunted church, a quiet, restful place where nobody would bother him because of the rats, which he didn't mind at all. And then he decided to show David the River Medlock. Some kids were rooting for scrap-iron in the river, and from one of them he learned that the Italians would be carrying the Madonna through the streets later on. This was something else he must show David.

The twelve men staggered under the weight of the Madonna; there were no flowers around her throne, for this wasn't the season for flowers. She swayed in the wind.

Michael held his statue up high. 'Look, David,' he told it. 'There's the Madonna, and it's a good thing for one statue to meet another statue, and that's Mary, and she's born of your line, which means she's your great-great-great-great-grand-daughter.' At that second, a tight hand gripped his wrist.

'Well, lad, that's a nice piece of pottery you're waving around,' said the new policeman.

Michael had always been given to understand that the animal on the left of the coat of arms was a unicorn, but when he asked he was told it was an antelope. There it was, poor little sod, chained up like a dog in a backyard. But the lion on the other side wasn't chained; oh no, it was free to kill and eat the antelope, which couldn't get away if it tried. Antelopes of the world unite, he thought to himself, you have nothing to lose but your chains. Ah, but wouldn't it be the hell of a thing now to have a pet antelope and be seen out walking it on Sunday; except there was no grass in Ancoats, and he guessed it lived on grass. Suppose antelopes ate lions, wouldn't it serve the lions for being lions? Suppose he had a pet antelope and it had baby antelopes, he'd be able to sell *Daily Workers* by shouting '*Daily Worker*, one penny! And get a free antelope with every one you buy! Don't miss your exciting free antelope!'

'Do you really expect the court to believe that this man, this Jewish pawnbroker, gave you this valuable piece of Dresden pottery?' asked the magistrate.

'Yes, master.'

'It might help you, boy, if you told the court just exactly where you obtained this ornament?'

'I've told you, master. Mr Ikey Mo of Every Street.'

'What a pity he's no longer there. Done a bunk, as they say.'

There was a waft of laughter. The magistrate adjusted his glasses and studied some papers on his bench. 'You're from Ancoats, I notice.'

'Yes, master.'

'You're not only a thief, you're a liar. I think a sound birching followed by seven years at a reformatory school, will do this little creature more good than harm.'

'Thank you, master,' said Michael, and his knees felt weak.

'Oh, and I think his parents should be made pay two shillings a week towards his upkeep at the reformatory. Get him out of my sight!'

Michael was dragged out of the Children's Court kicking and shouting. It was his parents he felt hurt about, for he knew his dad earned hardly any money, and would probably have to steal things in order to pay for him being at the reformatory. If only he could have gone with the Kennedy brothers to Australia, he'd probably be sending his parents money each week from the shearing of the sheep – like a real David, and not a pot one.

The first bites of autumn and the fast approach to winter were when Miss Daly put nightlights in her window to prevent the whitewash brush of frost from hiding her mouldy confectionery; and the lamplighter, who never talked to anybody because he didn't live in Ancoats, came with his pole before tea; and the library put its brown electric lights on, and its noticeboard talked of magic lantern shows; and the gangs ganged up and became ferocious shouting brigands, because it was time to start collecting wood for the Fifth of November bonfire night.

Nothing burnable was safe when the gangs, often as many as thirty men and boys, began their looting. Backyard doors were wrenched from the yards of those who couldn't stop them, like old people, sick people, and people whose menfolk had run away or gone to prison. The schools were broken into, and desks taken; the scrubbed forms in the clinic were sometimes hauled out in broad daylight; and the large wooden hoarding of a jolly man in striped pyjamas jumping over a five-barred gate to advertise Kruschen's Salts was pulled down and ripped up. There were some who said the school desks hadn't been taken for the healthy purpose of a bonfire, but were being cut up and boiled down to be turned into wood-alcohol for boozing.

Another sign of autumn was that the men drank more beer, mainly because the fires in beerhouse grates were better than the ones in their own homes; and the men usually stayed there until their wives and kids had gone to bed.

Kevin was surprised, therefore, when his dad came home half-way through the evening. Kevin had just returned from the library. His mother, with two shawls around her head and wrapped well around her, had started to peg a rug. She always pegged a new rug for Christmas Eve. Not being a Catholic, she didn't go to midnight Mass with Kevin and his dad. Her excuse was always that she'd still got a handful of rags to peg in; and when they came back there would be the new rug before the fire. She was just about to cut up a red coat which her husband had scavenged from a bin – all her rags came from the bins, including the canvas-sack base which this year said 'Jersey Potatoes'.

His dad thudded in, dropped himself on the chair, and began sobbing with his head lying on his arms folded across the table.

'And wouldn't ye be knowing,' he sobbed, 'just when ye're forgetting ye're Irish, there's summat terrible occurs what brings it all back to ye!'

'What's the blithering matter?' asked Kevin's mother, putting her arm around her husband's shoulders.

'Ach, the Devil ye should be asking,' he said; and then, more subdued, 'Will ye be pouring me a cup o' tea, m'cushla?'

'Aye, so I will, for the kettle's singing on the hob. But will ye be telling me –'

'Ye'll be hearing it soon enough. But ye might as well hear it now as later. 'Tis about Freddie Johnson –'

'He's a fine man, though not one of us.'

'I'll give ye there's few could have said much agin him. Till tonight, that is.' He moved his arms from the table and turned his chair in order to stare in the fire.

'That man's been sitting on the same stool in the same corner of the Spread Eagle for years now. Ach, we knew he was one o' them, and not one of us, but he paid his whack, and he joined in with some o' the songs – but not the rebel ones, d'y'know. And he'd lift up his pint to a "*Slainte*" any time of the day or night with any of us. Then in comes he this evening, and 'tis obvious from the start that he's the drink taken, even before he ordered his first pint, for his eyes is cock-eyed, and he's got the staggers and that, d'y'know. Then from outside in the cold air of the evening, the old blind fiddler starts up with "Kitty o' Coleraine". "'Tis a great little place is Coleraine," says Freddie. "And how could ye be knowing that?" says somebody. "Because haven't I been there?" says he. "You're not a mick, so how can ye have been in Ireland, lest you was in a uniform?" says somebody. "And maybe that uniform belonged to the King of England, and maybe 'twas in Ireland ye fought yer brave battles, and not in the muddy old trenches of Belgium and France at all?" "Here now," says somebody else, "come sup up yer pint, and I'll be buying yerz another. Was it with the Black and Tans ye were?" "Aye," says Freddie and ye could'a heard a pin drop. "And I shot me share of micks, I did and all," says he, and him putting his hands to his shoulder like he was holding a rifle. "Away, lads, and run for your lives, we'd say, and they'd be running across them fields while we

175

popped em off like rabbits." "Oh, ye did, did ye, and wasn't that something?" says somebody. "Come on away home now," says someone else, "for ye've had enough for tonight." And some o' them took him out to see him safely home. And 'twas the policeman came in half an hour later to say that Mr Johnson had been found murdered and dead in an entry with a knife in his back and a knife in his belly.'

'And who was them what took the poor man home?'

'Would ye be asking me to be answering a question like that, now?'

'He seemed a nice enough feller.'

'Aye.'

'He'd turn the mangle for an old woman if ever requested, and wasn't too proud to be shaking the peggy in the dollytub, and his hand was never out of his pocket for giving to the children. And isn't his own son in the same class as Kevin?'

'And 'twas no doubt 'twas his son's desk he'd been supping, for he was ranting and raving when he come in, and 'twas the liquefied desk as loosened his tongue. But I never found anything wrong with the feller, to be honest d'y'know.'

'And he'd put a new piece o' glass in the window for any one at any time, and only charge for the cost o' the glass.'

'And he picked up a ten bob note from the sawdust one night, and says he to me "It's yours?" and it was mine right enough, but 'twas civil of him to have told me, for sure I'd never have known till I came to count. But 'twas him and the likes of him drove many an Irishman from the green hills of Erin, and brought them to a place like this. He was a murdering, thieving, fornicating bastard in his little pom-pom, like the rest of the Black and Tans; but then I'd no idea the ten bob note had fluttered from me pocket. I harbour no grudge now the man is dead, but he was as nice enough a feller as you could be wishful to meet in a month o' Sundays. What beats me is why he came to live among us.'

'That's summat we shall never be knowing. And here's the mug o' tea you was asking for.'

'What's a Black and Tan?' asked Kevin.

'That's something ye'll need never to be bothering yer head about. And isn't it time you was toddling up the dancers on yer way to bed with them books under yer arm, and a candle to light you with.'

Kevin couldn't concentrate on his book; his mind was too busy trying to imagine what Black and Tans were, even though he and the other lads used to play at ambushing them with great slaughter. Their name sounded jolly, and they seemed like jolly men who danced around a lot; he could picture them on the music hall stage. 'And now, ladies and gentlemen, for your further pleasure this evening, we present those merry men of mirth, the Black and Tans! Give them a loud welcome, if you please!' And the curtain would open, and they would dance in to bright music, some of them doing back-somersaults, and others cart-wheeling. Then they would try to whitewash a room, but they would slap each other in the face with their brushes, and one of them would pour a tin of whitewash down another one's trousers, and one of them would drop a ten bob note, but it would be on long elastic, and would flirt out of reach when another tried to pick it up.

A little daisy showed its head,
And what do you think that daisy said?
Why, spring has come and don't you know
Now is the time when daisies grow.

Kevin thought what a daft song it was to teach the infants with winter coming on. Miss Cowgill should be teaching them something like 'Please to put a penny in the old man's hat'. It would be far more profitable to them with Christmas not far away. Arthur scribbled 'grow all in a po' on his blotting paper; he sniggered and passed it to Kevin. Kevin sniggered, and Mr Beaumont hit him on the forehead with the chalk. Timothy Johnson wasn't in class; his desk stood empty and on its own; the class took peeps at the desk even though they felt instinctively they shouldn't. Mr Beaumont left the classroom.

Grow, grow, all in a row;
Now is the time when daisies grow.

'Shall we go rail-riding after tea?' asked Kevin.
'If you like,' said Arthur.
That was the good thing about Arthur; he very rarely said no to anything, although it annoyed Kevin sometimes.
'And afterwards, shall we jump in the cut?'

'If you like.'

'You're a bloody stupid ignorant snotty-nosed Protestant bastard!'

'If you like,' sniffed Arthur, and started counting the wooden blocks on the floor.

Rail-riding was the next best thing to going on the green dragons. They climbed up the railway embankment at Palmerston Street, then hid behind a stack of oily railway-line sleepers. At the right moment, when the shunting locomotive had stopped and neither the driver nor the fireman was watching, they scrambled across to one of the empty coal wagons, climbed on to the buffers, and hoisted themselves into the wagon. The wagon had to be as near as possible to the locomotive to make it a longer and more exciting ride, for the man with the hooked pole unchained the trucks in ones and twos, and the locomotive kept jerking to a halt to send these unchained trucks down different lines. The wagon nearest the locomotive was obviously the last one to be sent rolling down the line. Inside the wagon they could only see the sky, and the thrill was that they never knew when the locomotive would stop with an awful, shuddering, squealing jolt and jerk them across the floor. The final thrill was when their own wagon would be released, for it would roll and roll, and go *kerklank* and *slam-bang* against some buffers. Added to that was the constant goose-pimpling excitement of maybe getting caught.

Kevin and Arthur dropped down into a wagon and lay flat.

'Harry Wharton, Sherlock Holmes, Dr Watson, Jeeves, Bertie Wooster, Raffles, Bulldog Drummond, Sexton Blake, Long John Silver, and Father Brown,' panted Kevin, without stopping for breath.

'Them's names,' puffed Arthur. 'Names what you told me about in books.'

'Aye,' said Kevin, 'and I might have to see the doctor, 'cos I can remember names of them I read in books, yet I forget names o' them as was me pals. He might give me pills for it, if me mam can afford it. There's pills for everything these days.'

'It's Beechams Pills you want, for you're talking shit instead of letting it come from your bum. It's daft.'

'No, it's not. It's a genuine disease, and people have been known to die from it. Sometimes the name of a kid goes right out of me head, yet I can tell you every detail of them in books.

Perhaps it's reading by candle what does it. Last night I couldn't remember the name of that kid what had an invisible dog, and his dad got hanged for killing his mam, and you and me walked to Strangeways the morning he was topped to hear the clock strike. And the paper said he read a book of fairy stories while waiting.'

'Terence.'

'That's right; I can remember it now. Perhaps it's when the wagon jerks and shakes me brains up. And then there was that kid what jumped in the river after that dog, and who was drowned, and who did the milk.'

'Sean.'

'Aye, but 'tis the wagon what's done it again.' Kevin wrinkled his forehead, and thought for a few seconds. 'Natty Bumpo,' he said.

'Who's him?'

'Lived out on the prairies.'

'What's my name?'

'Everybody knows your bleeding name, and if you don't know it yourself, I'm not telling you.'

The locomotive lost its temper; the steam huffed and puffed angrily, and, with another neck-breaking jerk, more wagons squeaked away.

'Nasty bumpo,' sniffed Arthur. 'We've just had a nasty bumpo on the boko.'

'And you'll be getting another one off of me if you try to be funny again, like them daisies growing in a po; I'm the one what suffers. I'm being dead serious.' Kevin thought once more. 'Sam McGee,' he said.

'What did he do?'

'Got himself burned to cinders 'cos he was cold.'

'I'd rather be cold than burned to cinders.'

'No, you wouldn't. Not in the Yukon you wouldn't.'

'How d'y'know?'

'I been there. In books,' said Kevin, and he recited:

There are strange things done in the midnight sun
By the men who toil for gold;
The Arctic trails have their secret tales
That would make your blood run cold.

179

He found that he was able to recite the entire poem right the way through.

> *The Northern Lights have seen queer sights,*
> *But the queerest they ever did see*
> *Was that night on the marge of Lake Lebarge*
> *I cremated Sam McGee.*

This was a hard job to do, for as he recited the shunting got stronger and stronger and shakier, and the coal dust on the floor of the wagon jumped up in black clouds and covered them and made them cough.

''Tis the most beautiful poem in the world,' went on Kevin. 'And you'll have to learn all that before we goes prospering in Canada. And sure we'll find more gold than they found in King Tut's tomb.'

'If you say so.'

'If I say so? Have ye no mind of your own? Are ye not desirous of being your own boss?'

'No. I like being bossed, and I like taking orders.'

'You're barmy! You'll end up like the mad monk.'

'It's just like you living in them books; only I sometimes see myself as a soldier in the Foreign Legion, and the officer says that one man has to stay behind and keep the fort against ten thousand wallah-wallahs on camels while the regiment escapes through the back door down an entry. And it's me.'

'You volunteer?'

'No, 'cos that'd be being your own boss. I'm picked. And I salute and say, "Yes, sir."'

'Then I tell ye what. If you come to the midnight sun with me, I'll order you to do the digging while I sit on me bum and talk to the pack mule.'

'When we get off the train,' said Arthur, changing the subject, 'me mam says you can come home with me for fish and chips.' There was always plenty of fish and chips at Arthur's these days; it was fish and chips for every meal; it was more than fish and chips, it was fish, chips and peas, sometimes even beans. Their standard of living had improved when his mother bought a red fox fur from the old pawnbroker just as he was closing down before the new man took over. A red fox fur meant that she looked posh; she could afford to forget trading at the Wine Lodge and was posh enough to sit at the bar of the Queen's Hotel, where she met richer men who paid her more.

The clang came. The locomotive jolted; the wagon shuddered, then rolled away on its own. The lads braced themselves for the coming crash into the buffers of another wagon. *Berlang!* They waited until the locomotive puff-puffed away, either to pick up some more trucks or to have its tea or whatever locomotives did when they'd finished one lot of shunting. Then they climbed over the side and dropped down on to the ground. They were about to slide down the embankment when Kevin found a haversack full of fog signals.

'This is almost as good as gold, and will buy a lot of herbal cigarettes,' he told Arthur. 'We can sell 'em to the gangs. They're explosives, and are better than a hundred fireworks when they go bang; they have to be, for the expresses to hear. All the kids will have to do is chuck 'em on the bonfire and stand clear. And we'll call 'em Cheltenham Flyers 'cos that's a crack express train and sounds a good name for a new firework, and not everybody likes Flying Scotchmen.'

> *Guy Fawkes, Guy,*
> *Hit him in the eye;*
> *Hang him from a lamp post*
> *And there let him die.'*

Although they sold all their Cheltenham Flyers, nobody would let them go to their bonfires, for the bonfire was sacrosanct. Football in the streets or robbing a shop – the churches were inclined to close a blind eye on mixing; no Protestant would split on a Catholic for robbery; no Catholic would deliberately foul a Protestant in a football scramble unless it was absolutely essential in order to score. But fireworks night was a different thing, for in the darkness and excitement a Catholic could stick a thunderflash in a Protestant's pocket quite easily and undetected, which was what Kevin said Zeus, who used to be God before God, was always doing to the ancient Greeks.

'How d'y'know?'

''Cos Miss Hindshaw told us on our Friday morning class in the museum, except you was too busy watching the shunting through the window.'

'I wasn't, I was counting the tiles on the floor.'

But it wasn't too bad not being allowed at anybody's bonfire, because as Kevin had predicted they not only made enough money on Cheltenham Flyers for herbal cigarettes but were able to buy some of Miss Daly's special treacle toffee and parkin cake and some bottles of sarsaparilla. Arthur's mother was going out for the night, so the house was theirs.

The pops, biffs, whiffs, bangs, crackles, crickles and zips sounded outside, and there was red glow from the rooftops of each street. And then there was an almighty explosion.

'That's one of the Cheltenham Flyers going off in Vivian Street, where that man went to prison for getting caught stealing,' said Kevin.

Later there was another explosion. 'That's Dundas Street where the woman killed her baby.'

The *dring-dring-dring* of a fire-engine bell sounded and stopped; an ambulance bell *drong-dronged* in the streets; and there was the *dingle-lingle-ling* of a police car. Another explosion boomed.

'And that's Fleetwood Street where that woman stripped all the clothes off of another woman in a street fight, and there was a collection for the winner.'

The fire-engine and ambulance bells became noisier and busier. Another bang rattled the windows.

'And that's Napier Street where the girl drank half a bottle of washing bleach. Or is it Grace Street where the man lost his eye? It isn't easy to tell, with all them bells going.' Kevin blew smoke rings, then prodded his herbal cigarette through the floating circles of light grey smoke.

'When ye come to think of it, 'tis a wicked bloody district, is Ancoats,' he said.

'Aye,' said Arthur, 'but it mightn't be for much longer, for by the sound of it them Cheltenham Flyers is blowing it all up.'

Considerable damage was done that night, and a casualty list was published in the paper, but Kevin and Arthur decided not to read it in case anybody had been killed.

Next day, the bell rang for a change of lessons, but instead of rubbing out 'Hundred Years War' and writing 'Geoffrey

Chaucer' on the blackboard, Mr Beaumont stood the class up and marched them into the hall. Other classes were shuffling into the hall as well. The general feeling was that somebody had died, but nobody knew who. The piano lid had been closed, so at least there wasn't going to be a hymn. The headmaster stood on the platform and watched the hall fill up; then he banged on the piano for silence. And then he called Kevin's name out.

Kevin had an immediate urge to run out of the school, and on to a railway wagon, and get to the Yukon and cover himself with snow. It was because of the fog signals. He knew what had happened to Guy Fawkes for trying to blow up Parliament; what, then, would they do to him for trying to blow up Ancoats? He felt hot and cold with each alternate split second. But he was unable to run. He walked slowly up to the platform. It occurred to him to blame Arthur if accused. The headmaster didn't use a cane, he used a thick leather strap; and Kevin wondered whether it would be his hands or his backside.

'History has been made in this school,' began the headmaster. 'In fact, history has been made in Ancoats. I have just been informed by the Manchester Education Committee that this boy standing before you has won a scholarship to a grammar school. I must congratulate him on behalf of the teaching staff, and I now ask you to show your appreciation in the usual manner.'

The children in the hall, pushed on by their teachers, clapped their hands; although there were some who made hidden farting noises. Kevin looked down at his boots. There was an excitement in him, yet he felt like a sissie and knew the others would be sneering at him because he was the kid who read books.

Later Mr Beaumont walked him into the cellar playground when everybody else was back at lessons.

'This is a great day for me,' said Mr Beaumont, 'for I've just won half a crown from each of the teachers, plus five shillings from Mr Rocca over in Saint Anne's. What do you think of that?'

'It's very good, sir. And must be over two pounds, sir.'

'It's a week's wages,' said Mr Beaumont. 'I said I'd get you a scholarship; they said never in a million years. It took me three years' hard labour at the University of Manchester to get one miserable kid to a grammar school, so I reckon I've earned that extra week's pay. What do you think?'

'Yes, sir.'

'The first scholarship to come out of Ancoats, eh?'

'Yes, sir.'

'And how long is it since your father brought you from Saint Anne's?'

'A year, sir.'

'You were dropped in my class like a goldfish in a clean bowl. You seemed to have something in you, so I bullied and even cheated you into reading.'

'Yes, sir.'

'Let's face it, coaxing and encouraging you would have got us nowhere.'

'No, sir.'

'So I badgered you.'

'Yes, sir.'

'Otherwise I would have lost a week's wages.'

'Yes sir.'

'And you're going to help dozens of boys and girls from Ancoats to do the same. There's another way out of the ghetto from now on, and it's called education.'

'Yes, sir.'

'Do you know how you're going to help them?'

'No, sir.'

'No, I don't suppose you do. You're a self-centred little beggar, and I can't see you ever coming back to teach in this school.'

'No, sir.'

Mr Beaumont smiled to himself, and the smile became a loud laugh, and the laugh echoed from the cellar arches. He held his stomach laughing.

'Because after the holidays the headmaster will make a stern little speech. And he'll say that if a boy can come from the Catholic school and gain a scholarship after only twelve months, then the children who began as infants at this school should do even better. He'll demand hard work for more and more scholarships. And across the road in Saint Anne's, their headmaster will be telling his school that if a pupil can be taken away from the school and get a scholarship in another school, then those at his school must work and do even better. Their headmaster will be afraid that more children will be taken away from his school and put in other schools, and the parish priest will feel the same. There will be a rivalry, not only between the schools but the parents, as never was known. A thing called homework will be introduced to Ancoats, and there'll be less playing out in the streets. You're the fastest gun in the Wild West.'

'Yes, sir.'

'Tell me, what do you want to become after you've left school?'

'A Dolly Varden man like me dad, sir.'

'Why?'

''Cos you find treasures in the middens, sir. Like it can be anything from a suicide's teddy bear, or a tin miller who climbs up a tin ladder with a tin sack of flour on his back, or a pair of slippers for me mam, even though one of them hasn't got a pink bobble, or a tin bus without the roof because the biscuits have been taken out and eaten, or a big book of ordinary survey maps of English counties showing churches and hill lines with Northumberland missing because it must have been somebody what didn't like Northumberland, or a book like *Moby Dick* which is hard to read and has too much about what makes whales and not enough about the captain, and tea-caddies without the tops of Queen Victoria as Empress of India, or a pointer dog with a stiff tail looking at a bright bird, or –'

'You'd better get back to the classroom,' said Mr Beaumont, 'otherwise I'll begin to doubt whether you got your elementary education from me or the middens.'

'I can't understand why I didn't pass to grammar school like you,' said Arthur when Kevin returned to his desk, 'for I got the same answers as you, because I copied them off your sum paper in the test, being as I'm no good at sums.'

'Did you do the working out?'

'No, 'cos you'd got your hand over the working. I just saw your answers.'

'But it said show all working.'

'How was they to know I didn't do it in me head? I scratched me head a lot, and the man saw me scratching.'

'That's 'cos you've got lice in your hair.'

The next few weeks were miserable for Kevin. Nobody would talk to him: it was as though he didn't exist. Aware of this, Mr Beaumont gave him tidying-up jobs like cleaning blackboards in empty classrooms and emptying wastepaper baskets. Worst was that nobody wanted to fight him in the street; if he thumped anybody to start things going, they just walked away as though they'd never been touched.

He called at Vera's house; she would be proud and probably give him a picture kiss. But he was told they'd moved to another district where there were privet hedges in front of the houses. Only Arthur remained loyal and friendly.

Kevin's parents were pleased. 'Sure education's a powerful thing, and even if ye can't get a job when ye leave school it'll help ye understand why ye can't,' said his dad.

'Ach, he'll get a job right enough,' said his mother. 'He'll become a clerk in the Town Hall, and wear a white shirt, and have a fountain pen in the top pocket of his coat, and he'll get a pension at seventy.'

Kevin had to be pushed out of the house on his first morning at the new school; he was shy in his brand-new uniform, which his dad had worked overtime to buy; in fact, the truth was he felt stripped naked rather than wearing smart clothes and a cap with a crest on it. Luckily he was too late for the mill girls and too early for the kids to be in the streets – they'd all have laughed at him. He waited for the tram outside the Horsfall Museum, and wondered if there was a kid in Brooklyn doing just the same that morning, for Brooklyn copied Ancoats, and he'd have more in common with that Brooklyn kid than he now did with the kids he'd grown up with. He got on the tram without anybody seeing him.

Baby, what I wouldn't do-oo-oo
With plenty of money and you-oo-oo.

A singing tram guard was the last thing he wanted. Ancoats was always singing; and they'd nothing to sing about. There was too much dead in Ancoats. People cried when they weren't fighting. He'd cried on the night he'd heard the little girl's hearse bobbing and clattering over the cobbles, and the sparks had sparked into the black blanket night air of the sweet-stinking river. If she'd lived instead of going off and dying like she had, she'd have been in the class when the headmaster said he'd brought honour to their school. Then there was the kid who'd cried when his dog was drowned in a tub; and another kid who'd cried when he went back to Ireland; and the kid who'd cried when the nun took him off to the orphanage because his mam had been killed; and they'd all cried when the policeman and that other kid were drowned in the flood; and they'd cried when Father Sullivan was buried; and they'd cried when that kid who sold *Daily Workers* had been carted off for seven years. True, they'd clouted each other in the face for catching each other crying like sissies. There was nothing to sing about in Ancoats.

> *Sing ho for the lord of the rushing wind*
> *As he leaps from his throne on high;*
> *With league-long pennants which stream behind,*
> *And coursers wild no thongs may bind,*
> *He sweeps through the midnight sky.*

The song from the music-room was a good song, a strong song; it wasn't about any kinds of love or Jesus; it was rushing and leaping and leaguing and streaming and sweeping and wild. The day had been spent in writing out timetables and getting books. Play-time was called break-time, and Christian names became surnames only, and 'attention' meant 'attention'.

When Kevin left school at four o'clock, he found most of the class waiting for him.

'By the sound of your name,' said somebody, 'you're a bloody little mick.'

'I'm Irish.'

'You can't be a bleeding Catholic?'

'On Sunday mornings – yes.'

'What does your dad do?'

'He's a Dolly – a muck – er, a Corporation dustman.'

'A bloody middenman?'

'Yes.'

'Where d'y'live?'

'Ancoats.'

There was a loud mock groan from all the group; some held their noses; some pretended to pull lavatory chains.

'Christ!' yelled someone, 'my parents would take me away from the school if they knew there was the son of an Ancoats midden-man in my form.'

'I thought there was a smell of cat shit in the classroom,' said another.

'You're a snotty-nosed bastard, aren't you? And I'll bet you wipe your nose on your sleeve, don't you?'

The group moved in on him. 'Go on,' said somebody, 'tell us you're a snotty-nosed bastard so we can all hear. Say "I am a snotty-nosed bastard from Ancoats, and my dad shovels shit for a living."'

Kevin went hot. This was how he'd talked to Arthur, and it was terrible. And Mr Beaumont had never warned him about this.

The circle closed in on him. 'Say it!' a number of the boys shouted. 'Say it!'

Without knowing it, Kevin strutted like a street fighter. 'I am from the West of Ireland, and my ancestors were kings of the same, and 'tis the lot of you'se put together I'll fight. 'Tis your bleeding skulls I'll be cracking, and it'll be me you step aside for, and make way for!' he shouted.

The boys moved nearer. He swung his long satchel around and around until it hummed. Occasionally it shuddered and thudded into a boy's face. He could no longer see individuals, just blurs of faces; they had to be stopped from moving; everything had to be made lie still; nothing had to move. Around and around and thud swung the satchel.

He stopped, exhausted and panting for breath. Some of the class had run away. Those left were lying on the pavement, most of them dabbing blood from their faces.

'We were only kidding,' one of them whinged. 'Can't you take a joke?'

'Shut up! Don't move, any one of you! If I see anything move, I'll kill it!'

Kevin didn't remember walking up the road, or catching the tram or travelling on the tram; he remembered getting off the tram. A gang from Saint Anne's was waiting for him.

'Get the bloody heretic, the bloody traitor!' one of them shouted. 'They say he's got brains; let's knock them out of him and see for ourselves!'

'Traitor to Saint Anne's!' they yelled.

He took off his jacket and cap and tie because they had cost money. Then he swung his satchel again. Once more, some ran; others were left slumped against a wall with blood coming from their faces. Nobody moved.

Further along Palmerston Street, another gang rushed at him. They were from his old class at Every Street.

'Get the bleeding Catholic what pinched a Protestant scholarship!' somebody shouted. Kevin took his coat, cap and tie off once more, folded them into a neat bundle, and windmilled his way into them, rushing and streaming and sweeping wild.

'And how was your first day at that fine school?' asked his dad. 'And what great knowledge have they pumped into your head, will ye be telling me?'

Kevin broke down in hysterics. 'I'll kill somebody, I know I will! And getting hanged isn't worth getting educated for! Take me away! I hate Mr Beaumont and the scouts at the Settlement and the Horsfall Museum and the library and all them books! But I've got to go back to Every Street School; I've got to go back; I want to go back! Or even to Saint Anne's! I've kept me uniform clean of blood, so ye'll be able to sell it. I want to go back to me old school, please!'

His mother said something would be done. She'd walk and keep walking until she found a house at a cheap rent away from Ancoats. But he'd have to stay at the new school, like it or not.

Arthur called for him to come out. Kevin walked with Arthur to the funeral yard of Aloysius O'Rourke, and when Mr O'Rourke wasn't looking, he stole two horseshoes from the nail on the wall.

'Are they for luck at the new school?' asked Arthur.

'In a way,' said Kevin. 'For they're to put in me satchel to give it the kick of a mule, for books on their own isn't hard enough to break jaws, and that's the only way a mick from Ancoats can get himself a civilized upbringing.'

He told Arthur his problems, and Arthur suggested they went back home for some herbal cigarettes.

'I daren't ever touch 'em again,' said Kevin, ''cos they make you feel half asleep the next day, and the First Form is all dead against me, but they're afraid of me, and I daren't ever be seen to be a dunce in front of them or they'll rip me to shreds with their tongues. I've got to beat 'em at everything all the time, including algebra and geometry.'

'What's them?'

'I don't know yet, but I've got to beat them at it all the time. So I can't touch them herbals any more.'

Kevin's mother found a house miles away where they'd not be

known, and it was arranged they would flit by handcart on a midnight, the hour of black darkness, to avoid the sneers and jeers and prying eyes of neighbours. The night was the same night as the opening of Collins' Wakes on Hilkirk Street croft, and Kevin got special permission to go to the Wakes with Arthur first; it was important for them to ride the green dragons.

The organs were *boop-boop-boop-dee-dah-daddle-dee-dee*, and the many steam-traction engines, flashing with brass rims, which surrounded the fairground, all facing inwards as though ready to advance and crush flat everybody on the croft, were *hiss-hiss-hiss*, and steam came from under their wheels, which stood higher than a man, even a man with a hat on. There were strings and streamers of coloured lights everywhere, and some lights stood still, and some went round and round, and some went up and down.

The lads were aware of the green dragons, but they didn't look at them; they kept their eyes away, for the dragons were to be saved until last. Oh, but they knew they were there, right enough, and they were sure the wild-eyed dragons were glancing at them as they rolled. The dragons were waiting to devour.

There were other things to be done first. The lads put pennies in the stock-exchange machine: when the handle was pulled down, three discs revolved, and if three commodities came up the same, money poured down through the slide. Arthur got cotton, rubber and wheat, and wheat, rubber and cotton, and other variations of those commodities. Kevin got tea, railways and wool, and he too was stuck with different arrangements of the same stock. As they walked away, an old woman put a penny in and got coal, coal, coal. 'And isn't that just what I needed,' she cackled, 'For 'tis coal is the very thing I'm wanting this raw weather.' But before she could collect the stream of pennies, a man pushed her aside, scraped up the money and ran through the crowd. There was general laughter, and somebody's voice shouted, 'Serve an old biddy like you right for gambling on the stock exchange!'

'Let it be a lesson,' laughed somebody else.

'You should be in bed saying your rosary beads, you silly old bitch.'

'At her age there's nowt else she can do in bed.'

The old woman laughed with the rest of them and shuffled off into the grey smoke.

It was time for the green dragons, and they stood and stared; they would watch them for a couple of times before getting on; it would work up their excitement. The heads of the dragons tossed and shook as they rattled and rumbled up and down the swift undulations; their mouths were redder and bloodier than ever; their unblinking eyes were merciless; their green scales glittered and reflected the many coloured flashes from the lights. The brass figures of knights and angels rattled their side-drums and lifted their trumpets; the organ music roared until everywhere throbbed; the dragons rolled faster. Kevin jumped with wildness.

'Come on,' he yelled. 'Liam, you take that one! Patrick, you that! Terence, there's yours! Sean, over there! Michael, ah Michael, get in that! Arthur, here!' He slowed down, and said in a natural voice, 'Arthur, this is ours, eh?'

'What you saying?' nudged Arthur.

'Nowt,' said Kevin.

'Yes, you did! You said the names of all the gang.'

'How the bloody hell could I? Sure I don't remember their names.'

'What time you leaving?' asked Arthur.

'Midnight.'

'Then I won't be seeing you again.'

'That's daft. I'll be coming back for the Scouts every week, and I'll be coming back for the Settlement parties, and I'll come on Saturday nights, and you can come to our house and stay the night. It'll be like coming on holidays for both of us, you see.'

'You'll forget me name, like you forgot the others.'

'I'll be smashing your bloody teeth in, talking like that.'

'When you leave school, will you be coming gold-prospering in the midnight sun?'

'I'm not sure,' said Kevin. 'Just finding gold gets you nowhere. I may become a clerk in the Town Hall. Trouble is, y'see, they don't teach you about digging for gold at the grammar school; they teach you more about Latin and French and triangles.'

The bell rang for the people to get on the dragons.

'Come on,' shouted Kevin. He turned to grab Arthur by the arm. But Arthur had gone. He was nowhere to be seen. He'd sneaked away. There was an empty dragon, and Kevin felt for his money. Then he turned and walked away and away, and away from the Wakes.

He kicked on Arthur's door, but the house was in dark. He went round to the back, hoping Arthur might be singing his candlelight hymn in the lavatory, but only cats were making noises. He felt sure Arthur was in the house. It was time to be going.

His mam and dad had stacked the handcart with their bits of furniture and belongings. The heap, tied by ropes, was so high and bulky that it looked loaded for a railway horse.

It was a bitter cold and frosty night; Miss Daly's nightlights had only made small circles in her frosted-up window. The frost on the cobbles was white and fluffy and glistening. His dad took his shirt off and flung it on the cart, spat on his hands, and grabbed the handles. Leaning forward, he tried to pull the cart, but his boots slipped on the frost. He knelt down and took his boots off; he never wore stockings.

'Are your feet not perishing, dad?' asked Kevin.

'Not at all. Why would they be? When I was younger than you, did I not have to bring the cows home across the wide Shannon when it was iced and there was a foot of snow, and there was no such thing as a pair of boots in all Erin? 'Tis the grip of your toes ye need.'

Kevin's mother walked in front with a lantern, and Kevin walked behind with a lantern, and all that could be heard was the rumble and crunching of the cart and the shunting of the railway wagons.

His dad stopped for a rest before lugging the cart up the steep Pin Mill Brow and under the Fenian Arch and out of the district.

Kevin's mother looked at the yellow gaslights they were leaving. 'And isn't that that?' she said. Then she prodded Kevin. 'Son, ye've lost the brogue of the old country, so maybe it'll be a good thing in future not to be telling the world you're Irish.' She looked to her husband for approval.

'Aye,' he said, 'for there's no money in being Irish, nor never was, nor never will be, and that's a fact.'

'And another thing,' said his mother. 'Wherever ye go, or whosoever ye talk to in the long days ahead, don't ye ever be telling a living breathing mortal soul that ye was fetched up in Ancoats.'